stick it

Jessie Frémont

Girl of Capitol Hill

Illustrated by Maurice Rawson

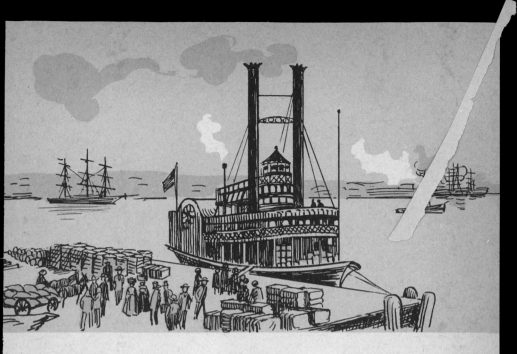

Jessie Frémont

Girl of Capitol Hill

By Jean Brown Wagoner

THE **BOBBS-MERRILL** COMPANY, INC.
A SUBSIDIARY OF HOWARD W. SAMS & CO., INC.
Publishers • INDIANAPOLIS • NEW YORK

*To my sister, Jessie, who
reminds me of the lovely
Jessie in this story*

Illustrations

Full pages

Numerous smaller illustrations

Contents

Books by Jean Brown Wagoner

ABIGAIL ADAMS: GIRL OF COLONIAL DAYS

JANE ADDAMS: LITTLE LAME GIRL

JESSIE FRÉMONT: GIRL OF CAPITOL HILL

JULIA WARD HOWE: GIRL OF OLD NEW YORK

LOUISA ALCOTT: GIRL OF OLD BOSTON

MARTHA WASHINGTON: GIRL OF OLD VIRGINIA

★ # Jessie Frémont

Girl of Capitol Hill

"Girls Can't Do Anything!"

"I DON'T see why Aunt Elizabeth had to have a girl baby," Frank said in disgust.

"I don't, either. Girls can't hunt buffalo or fight Indians or do anything," Charles grumbled.

"I'll bet there won't be any fireworks tonight now," muttered James.

"Yes, there will." The boys' little cousin Eliza, not quite three, spoke up cheerfully.

"No, there won't," James said. "Who ever heard of a celebration for a girl baby? I know Uncle Thomas is disappointed. He told everybody that this baby would be a boy. He'd already named it Thomas Hart Benton, Junior."

11

"I'm glad it's a girl!" Eliza said. She was nearly in tears. "Now I'll have a little sister to play with."

"We could cut off her curls and make a boy out of her," Charles teased.

This was too much for Eliza. She began to cry and ran into the house. The boys looked after her uneasily.

"You shouldn't make her cry," Frank said. "It always makes her sick. Now Grandmother will come out and scold us. She might even send us home. Then we'll miss out on the ice cream and cake, and the fireworks, too, if there are any."

"I'd hate to be sent home," James said. "I want to hear Uncle Thomas tell more stories about the West."

"I do, too," Charles added. "I've been counting on it."

This was May 31, 1824. "Uncle Thomas" was Thomas Hart Benton, the United States Senator from Missouri. He and his wife, Elizabeth, were staying here at her old home, Cherry Grove plantation, near Lexington, Virginia. As soon as he was sure that his wife and the new baby girl were all right, he'd go out west to the Benton house in St. Louis.

"Did you see the buffalo robe that Uncle Thomas brought Grandmother McDowell?" James asked. "He knows the man who killed the buffalo and skinned it."

"When I grow up, I'll go buffalo hunting," Frank boasted.

"I'll go along and scout for you, and watch for Indians," Charles added eagerly.

"Yah!" jeered James. "You don't know anything about scouting. The Indians would probably skin you."

"I'll get Uncle Thomas to ask one of the famous mountain men to tell me how to scout for Indians," Charles said.

"We'll all go home with Uncle Thomas one of these days," Frank cried out excitedly. "The hunters and traders in the West always buy their supplies in St. Louis. We'll see them and talk to them."

"Sure, and maybe we'll join one of their expeditions." Charles was wrapped up in the idea.

They were so pleased with this plan they forgot about Eliza. Suddenly James whispered, "Sh-h-h! I hear Grandmother coming. She's cross, too. Let's run!"

Without another word, they ran. In the wink of an eye not a boy was in sight. They escaped just in time. Grandmother McDowell came out the front door and marched around the corner of the porch as though she meant business.

"You boys ought to be ashamed of yourselves," she scolded as she went, "teasing Eliza until she cries. She's only half as big as you are, too." When she saw that the boys had vanished, a

smile came to her lips. "They knew they'd hear
from me." She chuckled.

Grandmother Sarah McDowell was a dainty
little white-haired lady with the sweetest, kind-
est face in the world. She didn't look cross at all.

Aunt Nancy, the Negro nursemaid, came right
behind Grandmother. She was big and broad.
Eliza, who clung close to her, was nearly lost in
the folds of her great skirt.

"Just let me at those boys," Aunt Nancy was

15

saying. She tossed her head. "I want to see who thinks he can take our baby away from us and cut off her curls. Just let me catch him!"

She frowned and shook her fist at the place where the boys had been. "They'd better run," she cried. "They know they can't fool with old Aunt Nancy." Then she turned to Eliza. "They were only teasing, honey. Next time they talk that way you laugh right in their faces and say, 'My little sister is the apple of my father's eye.' She will be, too."

"But they said Father was disappointed because he wanted a boy." Eliza's lip still trembled. She was a frail little girl, and easily upset.

"They're naughty boys," Grandmother said. "Don't pay any attention to them. Your father is as pleased as he can be. He loves your new sister. You run up to your mother's room and see for yourself."

Eliza, smiling now, went in and started up the

16

stairs. But at the top a tall, thin woman stopped her. It was Miss Emily, the English nurse-governess who had come with the Bentons from Washington, D.C. The Bentons lived in Washington during the winter while Congress was meeting.

"You must go back downstairs, Eliza," Miss Emily said primly. "No children are allowed up here. Your mother must have rest and quiet."

"B-b-but—" timid Eliza stammered—"Grandmother said——"

"You heard me." Miss Emily pursed her lips. "No children upstairs!" She turned Eliza around and made her go downstairs.

Eliza didn't run to tell her troubles to Grandmother again, but sat in a window seat in the back parlor and cried.

Uncle Dan, the oldest servant on the place, came by in a few minutes. He looked at her anxiously. He liked Eliza, because she was quiet and always wiped her feet before she came into the house. So now he said kindly, "Missy, why aren't you upstairs with your daddy, looking at the baby?"

"Miss Emily won't let me look." Eliza's tears rained down.

"You mean she won't let you see your own little sister?" Uncle Dan was so surprised that his eyes nearly popped out of his head.

Eliza sobbed, "Children aren't allowed upstairs."

Uncle Dan snapped his fingers. "Just you wait till I call Daisy," he said. She was the cook, and next to Grandmother the most important person in the household.

"What's going on here?" Daisy wanted to know, when old Dan called her into the parlor.

"That Miss Emily won't let little Missy see the baby," Dan explained.

Daisy didn't say a word. She gathered up Eliza in her arms and headed for Grandmother.

"It's time we found out who's boss around here," she muttered. She didn't like Miss Emily. The nurse wouldn't let her slip a piece of cake or pie to Eliza between meals.

Grandmother was talking to Eliza's Great-Aunt Edmonia, who had just arrived. She was startled at the sight of Daisy with Eliza in her arms, and Dan following.

"Old Miss," Daisy began, breathing hard, "that Miss Emily won't let our little Miss see the baby. And this poor child's been crying herself sick about it."

Then Grandmother started for the stairs. Great-Aunt Edmonia followed close behind, and Daisy came next with Eliza. Dan waited below. The little group was halfway upstairs when a bedroom door opened.

Senator Benton, smiling happily, stepped out. His face changed when he saw the crowd on the stairs. "Is Eliza hurt?" he called anxiously.

"No," Grandmother said. "But she's almost sick from crying. She wants to see the baby."

"Why, Eliza," her father cried, "haven't you seen your new sister yet? We'll take you in right now. The baby's asleep, but you can hold her, anyway."

Senator Benton lifted the baby from her cradle and laid her in Eliza's arms.

"Oh, see what funny faces she makes!" Eliza laughed aloud.

Grandmother and Great-Aunt Edmonia and Daisy smiled and nodded.

Miss Emily was not at all pleased. "The Bentons brought me with them to keep this very thing from happening," she said loudly to no one in particular. "How can I keep this baby from being spoiled, if every Tom, Dick, and Harry is allowed to cuddle her!" She gave a mighty sniff, and glared at the bedroom door.

As soon as everyone had gone back downstairs, Miss Emily went straight to Mrs. Benton. "I'll move the baby's cradle to the nursery," she said stiffly. "She'll have too much company if she stays in here."

There was no more trouble until that evening. Then relatives came by the dozen to congratulate the Bentons, for the Senator was an important man, and was well liked by his wife's people.

The father himself carried the baby around and showed her to everybody. Miss Emily didn't approve at all, but she couldn't say anything to the Senator.

That night there was a party with fireworks. Afterward, Senator Benton sat down to write a letter to his mother in St. Louis. He started to tell her about the baby. Then he put down his pen, scratched his head and frowned. Finally he went to his wife's room.

"Elizabeth, what's the baby's name?"

"She hasn't any name yet." Elizabeth Benton smiled. "We were so sure she'd be a boy, we chose only one name—Thomas Hart Benton, Junior. But I've been thinking all day about a name for her. Let's call her Anne, for your mother."

That pleased Senator Benton. He knew how proud his mother would be. "The only drawback is that Mother always said the name Anne was too short," he said. "It needs something in front of it."

His wife thought a little. "Your father's name was Jesse. Why not use that, also? We'll change the spelling, since it's for a girl. Let's see, Jessie Anne! I think that's pretty. It's unusual, too."

Senator Benton thought it was a beautiful name. He hurried back to finish his letter. Every now and then, though, he looked up, listened, tapped his foot nervously.

At last he put down his pen again and went to his wife's room. "Isn't Jessie Anne crying too much?" he asked. "I don't remember ever hearing Eliza cry like that when she was a baby."

"I kept Eliza with me," his wife said. "She was a sick baby and you could hardly hear her. But Miss Emily said this baby should be started right. She is going to keep her in the nursery."

"Should I go see her? Miss Emily may be asleep."

"I don't see how she could sleep with all that crying." Mrs. Benton sighed. She wished that Miss Emily had left the baby in the bedroom. Jessie Anne squawled and squawled.

"At least there's nothing wrong with her lungs," the father said. He paced up and down the room a few times, then started for the door. "I'll go and make sure she's all right."

Just then he heard voices in the hall. Aunt Nancy was calling, "Is the baby sick, Miss Emily? Do you want me to rock her?"

The door to the nursery flew open. "The baby is quite well," Miss Emily said crossly. And she shut the door in Aunt Nancy's face.

Jessie Anne howled on.

The father and the mother looked at each other. "Wait a little while," Mrs. Benton said. "Perhaps Jessie Anne will tire herself out."

A few minutes later Grandmother came and tapped at the nursery door.

24

"Miss Emily—" Grandmother's voice was clear and sharp— "what's the matter with the baby?"

The door opened. "The baby is perfectly all right," Miss Emily said calmly. "She was spoiled by the attention she got today. If we let her alone, she'll give up and go to sleep."

So Grandmother went back to bed. Jessie Anne cried on, and on, and on.

Finally Senator Benton could stand it no longer. "Spoiled or not," he said, "it can't be good for a baby to cry like that." He marched to the nursery door and pounded on it.

The baby's crying had kept the rest of the family awake, too. They heard the Senator go to the nursery, and opened their own doors to see what was happening. The door to the nursery opened last of all. Miss Emily seemed to have been asleep.

"Let me have the baby," Senator Benton said.

Miss Emily brought the screaming Jessie Anne to him. "I never saw such a household," she said. "You let one tiny, spoiled infant upset the whole family. If you start out this way, she'll be a real problem by the time she's walking."

"We don't let our babies cry," Senator Benton said. He carried Jessie Anne to his wife's room and laid the baby in her mother's arms. The baby gave one last little whimper and went to sleep. "The poor little thing was lonesome," he said.

"All she wanted was to be with people." Elizabeth Benton cuddled her.

Out in the hall Miss Emily sniffed. "All she wanted was to have her own way."

The house was peaceful now. In just one day Jessie Anne had certainly made herself heard.

Uproar in the Nursery

"I DIDN'T know what a good child Eliza was until Jessie came along," Mrs. Benton sighed one morning.

Jessie was seven years old. It was late spring and the Bentons were in St. Louis at Grandma Benton's house. Jessie's mother wasn't well and had to spend a lot of time in bed. Miss Emily had charge of the children.

There were four now. Another little girl, Sarah, had been born after Jessie. And the Bentons had a son, Randolph. The Senator had named him for his good friend, John Randolph, of Roanoke, Virginia. Miss Emily had plenty to do, but she said she could manage very well if it weren't for Jessie.

"I'm simply worn out trying to keep up with that child," Miss Emily complained to Mrs. Benton.

"Why, I didn't know Jessie had been any trouble after the day she was born," Senator Benton said, when his wife spoke of Jessie's naughtiness. "She seems the happiest, healthiest child we have."

"Nothing is wrong with her health." His wife laughed. "She's almost too healthy! But the only time she isn't into mischief is when she's asleep. She leads everyone a merry chase."

"Miss Emily should be able to control her," the Senator said. "I'm sure I could."

The mother only smiled. From what Miss Emily had told her, Jessie would be a handful for anyone.

"I wish you would try," Mrs. Benton said.

"Eliza is a very delicate child. It takes all of Aunt Nancy's time to care for her and me. Randy and Sarah are still so young that Miss Emily has to be with them. That leaves Jessie alone. I think she acts naughty just to get attention. No one has much time to spend with her."

Senator Benton was thinking that he didn't have much time, either. He wished he'd kept still. Aloud, though, he said, "I'll see what I can do to help." It was nearly time for the breakfast bell, so he kissed his wife and started downstairs.

Across the hall, Miss Emily was dressing the children. Randy and Sarah were both ready. Eliza and Jessie were nearly finished. Miss Emily was giving the last touches to Eliza's hair.

"Don't run away now, Jessie," Miss Emily said. "I want to comb your hair next. Sit here."

Jessie placed her chair directly in front of her sister and watched her closely.

"Don't stare at me so, please, Jessie," Eliza said. "You make me feel queer."

Jessie didn't seem to hear. She even stood up on her chair so that she could look straight into her big sister's eyes. Eliza squirmed and put her hands over her face.

"Jessie Anne Benton! Eliza asked you very politely to stop staring. Now stop it at once! I can't comb her hair when she's bobbing her head this way and that." Miss Emily was cross.

"I didn't make her move. I didn't even touch her," Jessie said. "I only want to see if it hurts."

Eliza dropped her hands. "See if what hurts?"

"If it hurts when she combs your hair. Your eyes don't squint, and you don't make faces."

"Of course she doesn't," Miss Emily said. "Eliza is a little lady. You ought to act like her. You're old enough to stop being such a baby."

"You don't pull her hair, and you do pull mine," Jessie said saucily.

"That's enough, Miss Jessie. No one could comb your hair without pulling, the way you dance around and jerk away. If you'd stand quietly, as Eliza does, it would be different. Even little Randy behaves better than you do."

"You don't pull his hair, either. I've watched, and the comb goes right through. His hair is smooth and straight like Eliza's. Mine twists around the comb, and you yank it."

"It isn't Miss Emily's fault that your hair is

curly," Eliza broke in. "Please don't mind it so much. Your hair is much prettier than Randy's or mine. It's so shiny it looks like fire when the sun shines on it, and it feels softer than silk." Eliza spoke gently, hoping that Jessie would not fuss with Miss Emily. Her sister always got the worst of an argument, and Eliza hated to see her punished.

"I wish we could trade heads," Jessie said. "Only I wouldn't want you to have my tangly old hair, either." She hugged her sister with all her might, for she loved Eliza dearly.

"Now see what you've done! You've mussed Eliza's hair, and I'll have to comb it again," Miss Emily fumed. "Really, Jessie, you try my patience to the limit. We're already late."

Just then Aunt Nancy appeared in the doorway. She often helped get the children ready for breakfast after she had brought their mother's tray upstairs. "You need me this morning?"

"Yes," answered Miss Emily shortly.

"Yes!" Jessie cried.

"Yes!" Randy and Sarah shouted together.

"Yes!" Eliza called happily.

Jessie and Randy and Sarah ran to Aunt Nancy. Eliza wanted to, but Miss Emily held onto her.

"Bring me a ribbon for Eliza's hair, Nancy," Miss Emily ordered.

"I'll get it!" Jessie cried, and dashed to the bureau.

"Never mind!" Miss Emily cried after her. "Let Nancy get it. You don't even know what color I want."

But Jessie had found the right ribbon.

"She knows what color suits Miss Eliza," Aunt Nancy bragged. "You can't get ahead of this child. She's smart and she notices things."

Miss Emily sniffed, and held out her hand for the ribbon. Jessie unrolled it and waved it in front of Miss Emily. "Here it is!" she cried gaily. "Take it!" But she snatched it back as Miss Emily reached for it. "Don't you want it?" she teased. She stuck it under Miss Emily's nose and jerked it away again.

Little Randy had been building towers with his blocks. He watched, round-eyed. Then he decided this was a game and joined in. "Give it to me!" he shouted. He grabbed for the bright piece of silk.

The fun was on! Around and around the room they went in a noisy chase. They climbed over chairs, scattered Randy's blocks, and dodged behind Aunt Nancy. Every time the little boy nearly caught the fluttering ribbon, Jessie waved it high in the air. Their laughter and the shouts and Miss Emily's scolding voice drowned out the sound of the breakfast bell.

Senator Benton heard the racket from the stairway and called that breakfast was ready.

"You'd better see what Jessie's up to," his wife called from her room. There was a crash inside the nursery as one of Randy's block towers went over. It sounded as if the house were falling down! Senator Benton ran to the nursery.

The sight of their father in the doorway made the children stop. Miss Emily was horrified. She didn't want Senator Benton to see the children or the nursery in such a mess.

Eliza was frightened and hid her face. Sarah and Randy waited to see what Jessie would do.

She rushed, overjoyed, to her father. "Oh, Father," she cried, "you're just in time to play with us. We'll let you be 'it' first."

Randy copied his sister, and hugged his father around the knees. "Be 'it!'" he shouted.

The Senator had intended to scold everybody. He didn't approve of the children being late to meals. And here they were, romping and playing, not ready to go down. But Jessie's dancing brown eyes were so full of joy at seeing him, he didn't have the heart to be cross.

"There's no time for games now." He tossed Randy into the air and caught him. "Breakfast is on the table, and Grandmother doesn't like for us to be late. If we don't hurry, the cook may think we don't want the food and carry it back to the kitchen. I don't want that to happen. I'm hungry."

"So'm I hungry!" Jessie cried.

"Hungry!" echoed Randy. They all hurried down to the dining room. Jessie's hair was still uncombed.

Breakfast was a cheerful meal. Miss Emily may have been a little more glum than usual, but no one noticed.

Jessie was the gayest of them all. "Maybe I can think up something like this every morning," she said to herself. "Then I won't ever have to have my hair combed."

"I'll Live by Myself!"

AFTER BREAKFAST Senator Benton asked Miss Emily to come to the library. Aunt Nancy took the children into the garden.

In the library Miss Emily poured out her troubles with Jessie. "When she has her own way, she's as sweet and lovable as a child can be," she told the Senator. "But when we disagree she seems to look for trouble. Mostly it's mischief or carelessness. She's never ready to put her playthings away. No matter how many stories I read at bedtime, she always begs for 'just one more' before she goes to sleep. She sets a bad example for the others, especially Randy.

"But my worst trouble is combing her hair. That's what started the uproar this morning."

"Can't Aunt Nancy help you with Jessie?" the father asked.

Miss Emily shook her head. "Nancy is no help at all. She thinks the children are little angels. If I didn't watch, she'd give them sweets at all hours of the day. Jessie is her favorite. If I have to punish the child and make her stay in her room alone, Nancy brings her cookies and milk, and slips in a puppy or kitten for her to play with. She's more of a hindrance than a help. She spoils Jessie more every day."

Senator Benton listened to all Miss Emily had to say. He thought Jessie was hardly as bad as the nurse said, but he knew she'd have to mind Miss Emily. He didn't allow his children to stay up late. He didn't want them to have sweets between meals. It wouldn't do to let Jessie have her way. Miss Emily had to be in charge.

"I'll talk to Jessie the next time you have trouble," he promised. "Send her to me, and I'll see what I can do."

Then he turned to his desk, for he had several letters to write and speeches to plan. He sincerely hoped his second daughter had done all her mischief for one day.

He spread out his papers and sharpened his pens. He was ready to begin, when he heard a tap at the door.

"Who could that be, at this time of day?" the Senator muttered. Everyone in the household knew this was his study hour. No one was supposed to bother him in the library. He waited a moment. Perhaps he'd imagined that he heard the tap. But just as he turned back to his papers, another tap came. Half angrily he rose and threw open the door.

"Why, Jessie!" he said, surprised. He'd already forgotten his talk with Miss Emily. "Don't you remember that I don't want visitors when I'm busy in here?"

"Yes, I remember," Jessie said. "And I told Miss Emily you wouldn't like it, but she made me come, anyway. I'll tell her what you said." With a little curtsy, she started away.

"Oh, wait a minute," her father called. His talk with Miss Emily had come back in a flash. "Why did she make you come?"

"I won't let her comb my hair."

"Why not?"

"It's too late now." Jessie looked up at her father through her long eyelashes. "We always have our hair combed before breakfast."

"That's a silly excuse, Jessie Anne. I'm ashamed of you." He frowned at her tangled curls. "Your hair looks awfully messy. Why don't you let Miss Emily make it neat and pretty?"

"But she hurts me! When she combs my hair,

she pulls till I cry." Jessie nearly cried, just
thinking of it.

"I'm sorry for that, but you know you must
have your hair combed. The rest of us don't go
around looking like frights. If you want to look
like that, you'll have to live by yourself."

Jessie thought a minute. It might be fun to

live where Miss Emily couldn't bother her. "Where would I go?"

"You would stay right here. But you'd play by yourself and eat by yourself. You couldn't even talk to any of us."

"Would I have to eat in my room?" Jessie knew she wouldn't like that.

"No, you'd go downstairs, so Aunt Nancy wouldn't have to carry up another tray. But you'd have to sit in the pantry where you couldn't see us."

"Could I play in the garden?"

"Yes," her father said, "but only when Randy and Sarah and Eliza aren't there." He let her think this over. "Which do you want? Do you want to be one of the family or live by yourself?"

"Do I have to have my hair combed?"

Her father nodded. "Every morning," he said, "or whenever it needs it—and you must let Miss Emily comb it without complaining."

"I think I'll live by myself," Jessie decided.

"Very well," her father said, "I'll tell everyone. No one is to have anything to do with you until I say so. If you change your mind, come and tell me." Then he closed the door.

As soon as he was sure the little girl had gone, he went to tell his wife and Grandma Benton what he had done.

"You've found the right way to manage Jessie," said his wife. "We know she loves to be with people. I don't believe she'll enjoy living by herself so much as she thinks she will."

Jessie's father wished he could be sure of it.

Home Again!

JESSIE SKIPPED down the hall to her room. She was glad she had decided to live by herself while it was still early in the day. There were many things she wanted to do, things that Miss Emily didn't allow.

First she went into the guest room, where a great four-poster bed stood. On it was a high featherbed, which looked very soft. Father said featherbeds weren't good for children to sleep on. But Jessie had always wanted to jump right in the middle of one. So today she climbed up the little steps at the side of the bed and gave a mighty leap into the middle of it.

"Whee!" It was even more fun than she'd thought it would be. She sank so deep into the featherbed that she couldn't see out. It was like being buried in a snowdrift. She stood up and fell forward into the downy pillows, and then backward and then sideward.

"I must tell Randy," she thought, "and let him try it. He'll laugh and laugh and laugh." Jessie climbed down from the bed and went to find him.

Then she remembered that she couldn't talk to him. "Oh, dear!" she thought. "That takes half the fun out of it." She decided not to play on the bed any more.

What to do next? It had begun to drizzle outside. "I know what I'll do!" Jessie thought. Every time it rained, she begged to go out. She wanted to jump puddles and shake bushes to feel the spray in her face. Now there was no one to forbid playing in the rain.

She raced down the hall to the top of the stairs, then stopped. No one was looking, so she hopped astride the banister and slid down. It was such fun she let out a loud "Whoopee!" That was what western hunters yelled at the buffalo.

Outdoors it was great sport, at first, to jump up and grab branches and make raindrops shower down. It was jolly, too, to watch the water splash when Jessie jumped into a puddle.

None of it was so exciting as she had thought it would be, though. It was a lot more fun when Miss Emily was scolding and fussing at her. She began to feel chilly. "I'll climb one tree, then go in and get warm," she decided.

Climbing trees was one thing her father allowed her to do in spite of Miss Emily's disapproval. He thought it was good exercise for girls as well as for boys. Miss Emily said that no little girls in nice families did it. It wasn't ladylike. But Senator Benton said he didn't care. As long as his daughters were well-mannered, and kind and gentle, they could run and climb all they wished.

This morning Jessie climbed higher than she had ever gone before. "Hurrah! I can look down the street over the garden wall, and see our neighbors' yard and stables. That's the Mississippi River away out there!" she shouted.

"I'll sway the limb so it'll hang out over the

wall, and if anyone comes by I'll shout, 'Hello!' Won't that surprise them! I hope Miss Emily is watching." Jessie began to swing with all her might.

She swung too hard. The branches high in the tree were small. They didn't sway. They swished, and nearly shook her loose. The bark was slippery with rain. One minute Jessie was on top of the limb, and the next, she was underneath.

If Miss Emily had been down below, shrieking to her to come down, Jessie would have enjoyed scaring her. But now she was frightened and held on for dear life. If anyone passed, she was too busy hanging on to notice.

At last the tree stopped thrashing around. Jessie slid slowly and carefully to the ground, and looked at herself. No bad scratches, no bruises—but oh, her clothes! "Miss Emily will make me sorry for this," she thought. Then she remembered that Miss Emily wouldn't even see her.

"I wish she would see me and say something," Jessie said aloud. "I'd rather have someone around. Even if it's someone who's mad at me, it'd be better than doing things alone. Nothing's any fun, if nobody cares." She was ready to cry.

Then a happy thought came to her mind. "I'm so hungry that it must be lunchtime. I'll run in and dress and be ready. Miss Emily and Eliza won't believe their eyes when they see me come in without a scolding." Usually Miss Emily had to coax and fuss to get Jessie indoors at all.

It felt good to put on warm, dry clothes. Jessie sat by the fire and waited for the bell. She waited and waited and waited. It seemed awfully quiet in the house.

"Maybe they're eating now," Jessie thought. "Of course, that's what's happened! The bell rang while I was in the tree." She slipped downstairs and listened at the dining room door. There wasn't a sound. "They're already through!" she cried unhappily. "I've missed lunch. Oh, and I'm so hungry! I don't think I can wait till dinnertime." She looked at the clock in the hall to see how long that would be.

Her eyes grew big when she saw the hour hand. It was only ten o'clock. It had to be later than that! The clock must have stopped. But no, the hour began to strike. Bong! Bong! Bong! Bong! Bong! Bong! Bong! Bong! Bong! Bong!

It would be a long, long time yet until lunch. Jessie had never known a whole day to go so slowly as this morning had gone. If there were only someone to talk to or play with!

She crept back upstairs and listened at the nursery door. Miss Emily was reading a story aloud. It was one of Jessie's favorites. She heard Randy laugh and clap his hands. She stayed there and wished she were inside with the others. They sounded cheerful and pleasant.

Suddenly voices reached her from the front bedroom. Violet and Milly, the two upstairs maids, were talking. "Look at this bed! It was that Jessie Anne who did this! Nobody else would do such a thing!"

"She jumped up and down on it with her shoes on. See the black marks! We made it up all fresh just yesterday, too. I'd like to be the one to comb her hair a few mornings. She wouldn't climb on my pretty, clean spreads another day."

Jessie decided she'd better get back to her own room and stay out of sight.

It wasn't cozy in there any more. Her wet clothes were lying on the floor, just as she had left them. Her bed wasn't made. Even the fire had gone out. Jessie leaned against the window-pane and looked down into the street. A carriage was waiting at the front door.

"Why, that's our carriage!" she cried. For a terrible moment she thought the rest of the family was going for a ride, leaving her behind. Then she saw her father go out of the house.

Jessie wished she were going with him. It was such a lonesome old day. She wished she'd never said anything about living by herself. How could she wait till he came home?

"I won't get to talk to anybody until suppertime." Jessie sighed. Then her face brightened. "Maybe I can catch Father right now. That's what I'll do. Tell him now!" She burst out of her room, and raced downstairs, shouting all the way, "Father! Father! I want to tell you now!"

She reached the front door and pulled at the handle with all her might. "Somebody help me!" she cried breathlessly. "Quick! Before Father starts." The door wouldn't budge. "I can't open it by myself," she sobbed. "Father's leaving, and I want to tell him I'm going to be good."

No one came. Violet was in the back hall and
heard her. She was still cross about the featherbed, and pretended she didn't hear. "Why
should I put myself out?" she muttered.

Jessie kept yanking at the door. Finally it
came open, and she dashed out.

"Wait, Father, wait! It's Jessie Anne! I don't
want to live by myself! I want to tell you!

I——" She was an instant too late. The carriage was already moving down the street.

Jessie watched it disappear. She didn't cry, but a big lump came into her throat. It wouldn't go down, no matter how hard she swallowed. Her head ached. She started back into the house. But the door had closed behind her and latched. She couldn't get it open.

"Oh, well, I won't go back there, then!" she cried. "Nobody misses me. I'll run away. I'll run away and never come back. Then maybe they'll be sorry." Jessie didn't give a thought to which way she'd run or where she'd stop. "I'll hide in the stable until it's dark. Then I'll run all night."

She started across the garden to the stable. She ran to keep warm, for it was turning colder, and her clothes were soaked through again.

She was beginning to wish she could wait to run away on a warmer day. She even wished she didn't have to run away at all. She thought of her sick mother. It might make her mother worse if no one could find Jessie at lunchtime. Father would feel bad, too, if she didn't even tell him she was sorry. She stopped running.

"Miss Jessie! Oh, Miss Jessie!"

The little girl stared. Was she hearing things? The wall was talking to her! She looked and looked again. The wall wasn't talking—it was Aunt Nancy! She came through a gate in the garden wall.

"Miss Jessie," Aunt Nancy scolded, "I thought I would never catch you. You come into the house with me." She was shooing Jessie ahead of her and acting awfully cross. That didn't worry the little runaway a bit. Aunt Nancy was only fooling.

The old servant hurried the little girl upstairs and helped her get into dry clothes. She fussed at Jessie all the time. "Running in and out of the rain! Skinning up and down trees! Scaring me half to death!

"Now, you go see your mother," she said when Jessie was dressed. "Tell her what it was you wanted to say to your daddy. I heard you calling, but I couldn't get downstairs fast enough."

Jessie didn't know that Aunt Nancy hadn't let her out of sight since breakfast. Nor did she know that her father hadn't left the house until he had seen her come safely inside.

All Jessie knew was that she didn't ever want to live by herself. She told her mother so over and over again.

"I'll let Miss Emily comb my hair all day, and I won't fuss or make any noise, no matter how hard she pulls. I'll never jump on the bed again, either. I'll be so good you won't know I'm in the house!"

Her mother hugged her then and said she hoped Jessie wouldn't be that good. "Now, if you'll bring me the comb and the brush from my bureau, I'll see if I can get some of the tangles out of those wet curls."

While her mother brushed and combed, Jessie talked. "I wish you could do my hair all the time." She sighed. "You pull, but it doesn't hurt the way it does when someone who's mad at me pulls. Miss Emily's always mad at me."

"Maybe if you were kinder to her, she wouldn't have to be cross," the mother said gently. "That would make it pleasanter for all of us. It worries your father and me to hear her scolding and your crying. We know then that you've been naughty. When we hear you laughing and playing, the whole day is brighter. Your father smiles and says, 'Jessie brings sunshine into the house.'"

That made Jessie feel happy and warm inside. "I won't forget. And I'll try very hard to be nice to Miss Emily," she promised. "Now I want to go tell Grandma Benton." Jessie ran out of her mother's room.

When Aunt Nancy brought the lunch tray, Mrs. Benton told her that Jessie was going to live with the family again. "Will you ask the cook to set Jessie's place in the dining room? Let Miss Emily know, too, please."

Aunt Nancy went to the nursery first with the news. Eliza and Sarah and Randy jumped for joy. They always had more fun when Jessie was around.

In the days that followed, Jessie proved that she could be good. Even Miss Emily was surprised. She had to admit that her naughtiest child was easier to live with. There were no more wild games in the morning, no arguments about putting away toys, no excuses for staying up at night.

For Jessie had decided it was much better to get along with people than to do without them.

What's Wrong with Jessie?

THE NEXT spring the Bentons were living in Washington, because Congress was meeting. Once again Mrs. Benton had to talk to her husband about Jessie. "I think the child spends too much time by herself," she said. "She seems lonely, and she's as pale as a ghost."

Senator Benton looked startled. "Is she sick?" he asked.

"I don't know," his wife replied. "But I'm worried about her. So is Aunt Nancy. Even Miss Emily has spoken about it. Jessie doesn't eat very much, or play, or fuss, or make noise. She's just too good."

"How long has she been like this?" the Senator asked anxiously. "Why didn't you speak to me sooner? Where is Jessie now?"

He didn't wait for answers to his questions. He headed straight for the room where the children were.

When Senator Benton reached the door, he saw that the children were already dressed for breakfast. He suddenly realized how different the whole scene was.

Jessie was standing absolutely still while Miss Emily combed her hair. The other children were sitting beside the fire. No toys were scattered about. No chairs were turned over. Everything was in order.

"Well, well," he called out cheerily. "Ready early, aren't you?"

"We're always ready, now that Jessie doesn't upset us," Miss Emily said.

"Is that what's the matter?" the Senator asked.

"I thought you all must be sick, it's so quiet. Step up here, Randy. Let's see if you're sick! Stick out your tongue."

Randy was pleased to show off. He stuck his tongue out so far and opened his mouth so wide that his father pretended to be afraid. He jumped back. "Close that mouth quickly before I fall into it!" he said.

Sarah came next, then Eliza. Senator Benton noticed that his oldest daughter was pale and thin, but she'd always been that way. She didn't seem any worse.

"Now, Jessie, let's look you over," he said cheerfully. There was no doubt about it; she had changed. Her face was pale and seemed to be all eyes. Her father was worried. He didn't want his Jessie to look like a little ghost. He didn't let her see that he noticed any difference.

"It isn't time for the breakfast bell," he said. "Have you had your morning exercise?"

No, they said, they hadn't. They didn't even
know what he was talking about. This was the
first they'd heard of morning exercise.

"What!" Senator Benton said. "You don't
know about exercise? Miss Emily, open the windows! Everybody line up," he ordered. "Now
face the windows and take a deep breath. Hold
it! Now let it out slowly."

There was a great sucking in of breath by
Randy and Jessie. They had a contest to see

who could make more noise and take longer to let their breath out. Eliza and Sarah were quieter about it.

Randy looked like a butterball, with his cheeks about to burst and his fat little stomach stuck out. Jessie couldn't keep from giving him a poke in the middle.

"Poooooffff!" Out went the air, and down went Randy's cheeks.

Eliza laughed. "Oh Randy, you sounded just like a balloon."

"Like a balloon!" Randy shouted. "Do it again, Jessie!"

"Poooooooooooofffffffff!" he went when she touched him.

In a minute everybody was being a balloon. Randy's cheeks were reddest, but Jessie's were next. She began to look more like herself.

The next thing their father had them do was whirl their arms like windmills. "Now stand in a row again, and bend and twist like trees in the wind!"

"I know what that's like!" Jessie cried. She remembered how the tree in the garden had moved that day in St. Louis. She showed the others. Jessie didn't look the least bit like a ghost now.

The breakfast bell sounded.

"Line up! Line up, everybody," the Senator ordered. "Miss Emily, look at their hands and see if they're clean."

She did, and said she thought they'd do.

"Now, then," the Senator continued, "you're to do this every morning. Open the windows, take deep breaths, and bend and twist like the trees. You'll have to be quick about it, because you must be on time every morning. Will you remember?" He looked at each child, and each child nodded. Then he threw open the door.

"We must be quiet in the hall," he said. "This

kind of fun in the house is to be only at exercise time. We'll walk past Mother's door, so that she can see how well you are!"

They all waved and threw kisses at her as they passed. Their mother waved and smiled back. She was holding the baby, Mac, on her lap. The youngest Benton was almost a year old now. He had been named James McDowell, for his grandfather, but everyone called him Mac.

After breakfast the Senator started upstairs to work on a speech. The children went upstairs, too. They had lessons with Miss Emily each morning. Even Randy and Sarah had paper and crayons, and pretended to write. Eliza and Jessie had reading, writing, and spelling.

"Miss Emily, must I have lessons today?" the Senator heard Eliza ask. "My head hurts."

"Oh, dear, you'd better lie down then, Eliza," Miss Emily murmured. "You probably had too much exercise. I was afraid of that. I'll send

Nancy to you right away." Miss Emily knew that Eliza didn't complain if she could help it. "The rest of us will be very quiet, won't we?" She turned to the other children. "Jessie, you go back downstairs and learn your spelling quietly by yourself in the parlor. I'll keep Randy and Sarah with me."

"Does it hurt very much?" Jessie asked.

Eliza tried to say it didn't, but she looked sick. Jessie began to look sick, too. She hated to spend the day alone, but she didn't say anything because she was still trying to be good.

Senator Benton was watching from the top of the stairs and saw her face. "If Jessie is sent off by herself every time Eliza is sick, I'm not surprised that she's grown pale and thin," he thought. "Jessie loves to be with people. She isn't happy when she's alone."

He called, "Let Jessie bring her speller and come to the study with me."

He was glad to see his daughter's face brighten, but he felt a little worried, too. He hoped Jessie would be quiet so he could work.

She bounced into the study right on her father's heels.

"Where's your book?" he asked.

"I don't need it," she replied. "I know all the words by heart. I'll spell today's lesson for you." She began, "Treasure, t-r-e-a——"

But her father stopped her. "That's enough!" He covered his ears.

"Don't you like to hear it?" She giggled at the face he made.

"I already know it," he said. "Let's see if we can find something more interesting for you." He began to look among his books.

This suited Jessie. She'd never liked the speller. The words weren't very interesting. It was nice to know that Father didn't seem to think they were interesting, either.

Senator Benton hoped to find a book with pictures in it. While he hunted, Jessie piled fat books on a chair at a table beside her father's desk. Then she climbed up and sat down.

"I like this room," she said. "I'll sit here every day and help you study." There was a map spread out on the table. Jessie held it flat and leaned over it and began to sound out some of the words printed on it.

"Father," she called in a minute, "I can read this! Look! It says O-h-i-o R-i-v-e-r. I know about that. I've been there. That's the way we go home to Missouri!"

Her father stopped his search and came over to the table. Jessie was running her finger down the line of the Ohio River. Suddenly she cried out excitedly, "There's the town of Wheeling, right here on the river! When we go to Grandma Benton's, we ride in the stagecoach to Wheeling. That's where we get on the steamboat. I remember, because last time I dropped my doll in the road there, and I cried because Miss Emily wouldn't let me go back and get it."

"Why wouldn't she let you?" the Senator asked angrily.

"Because there were crowds of people waiting at the landing. They stood back to let us get on the boat first. Miss Emily told me not to be a bother, because so many people were waiting for us to go aboard."

"The next time you call me, if you lose your doll," Senator Benton said.

"Oh, I won't take my doll the next time," Jessie said happily. "I'm taller now. I can stand up and look out the windows. I won't want to play dolls. I'll want to see everything."

Her father was thinking that a coach trip wasn't much fun for a little girl who had to sit inside and couldn't see out. It took several days to get to Wheeling. Then the family spent a week or more on the steamboat before they finally reached St. Louis. No wonder Jessie had cried when she lost her doll.

"If we go to St. Louis next year," he said, "I'll let you sit with me up on the coachman's seat. I'll take you to the top of the boat, too. Then you can see everything."

This was almost more than Jessie could stand. "Oh, let's go to St. Louis right now," she begged.

Her father laughed. He explained that he couldn't leave Washington while Congress was meeting. "We couldn't travel now, anyway. There's been too much rain. The Ohio River has overflowed its banks. It has spread so far that the pilots on the river boats can't tell where the channel is. The roads near the river are under water, too, so we couldn't get to Wheeling.

"We can talk about St. Louis, though." Senator Benton smiled. "I'll tell you a story about it."

"I like your stories better than books," Jessie

71

said, honestly. But she was also hoping that Father might forget about her lessons.

The Senator looked pleased. Then he leaned over the map and pointed to a wide, twisting line.

"See—here's the great Mississippi River. Down this river, way back in 1700, came some French missionaries. They were looking for a good place to build a mission. They wanted to preach to the Indians and persuade them to become Christians. The missionaries found friendly Indians at this bend in the river. So they stopped right here."

"At St. Louis?" said Jessie in surprise.

"Yes, but it wasn't named yet. There wasn't even a town yet at this spot. The missionaries stayed for three years, then moved on to build other missions. And the river bend was deserted again for more than fifty years. Then other Frenchmen settled in the same place. These were traders, who'd come up the river from New

Orleans. They brought all sorts of goods to trade with the Indians for furs. And soon their trading post grew into a French village. The traders called the new village St. Louis, in honor of a French saint. You see, all the land west of the Mississippi River once belonged to France."

"Is that why so many French people live near Grandma Benton now?"

Her father nodded. "St. Louis was a happy, peaceful town, and the French settlers loved it. They built a cathedral and then a school there—remember? You've seen those old buildings.

"But in 1803—I was just a young man in Tennessee then—a most unusual thing happened. The ruler of France needed a great deal of money, and he sold all of those western lands to the United States, for fifteen million dollars. So now the city of St. Louis belongs to our country. And many Americans, like our own family, have gone there to live."

"I'm glad the French people didn't leave after France sold St. Louis," said Jessie. "I like them. There's Madame Savary, who taught us how to do fine sewing, and Monsieur Savary, who gave me French lessons. And Madame Auguste, too. I like her because she always calls to Eliza and me when we're on our way to Madame Savary's. She invites us into her garden, and her maid brings us hot chocolate."

"I like to think that our trappers and hunters still come to St. Louis to trade and get their supplies, just as they have for many years," her father said. "St. Louis is still the gateway to the West."

Jessie was listening, but at the same time she traced the Mississippi with her finger.

"Father!" she exclaimed suddenly. "Did you know that St. Louis is at the edge of the world?"

Senator Benton looked startled.

"See? Here it is on the river. On this side

are lots of cities and towns. On the other side, in the West, there are hardly any names."

"There's plenty of good land out there, though!" her father said. "That's wonderful country west of St. Louis. People used to think it was all desert and stony mountains, not worth much. But explorers like Meriwether Lewis and William Clark, and Zebulon Pike, and Lewis Cass, and Jim Bridger have proved that there are thousands of acres of rich farmland and great forests and rivers and lakes, besides the Rocky Mountains and the desert."

"But there aren't many towns or forts on this map," Jessie said. "Why don't more people live out there in that fine country?"

"They don't know enough about it yet," Senator Benton told her. "Some explorers have made maps and written reports of what they found, but not many."

"I don't see why maps make much difference," Jessie said. "I'd just head west and keep going until I found the place I wanted."

"What if you came to a stream with such steep banks you couldn't get your wagons down to the water without tipping them over? What would you do?"

"I'd walk along the edge of the bank until I found a level place. Then I'd go back and drive my wagons there and take them across."

Her father smiled. "You'd probably have to

cut down trees and build a road to the crossing place," he said. "You'd lose a lot of time. A well-marked map would show you exactly where to cross and how to get there."

"Maybe the place I'd find would be better than the one on your map," Jessie said. She was pleased with her argument.

"Suppose you drove your oxen or horses across that level place and they began to sink? It might be quicksand, you see."

Jessie looked sad. "The nice horses would drown. Oh, Father, that's not fair."

"Traveling through new territory is not easy," her father answered. "The right kind of map will show settlers how to get to the good land in the West. Explorers' reports are important, too. They should tell where friendly Indian tribes are, and where there's good fishing or plenty of game. They should tell the farmers what kind of soil they'll find along the way."

"Why don't the reports tell these things?" Jessie asked.

"There isn't enough interest in the West," her father replied. "A few men have explored parts of the country. Some maps have been made. But no one has had quite enough information. Men who go west want reports and maps which are simple and practical. They want them to show natural landmarks—stream crossings, bends in the rivers, odd-shaped rocks.

"Someday the right man will come along who'll make the kind of maps people need. He'll be a scientist and an explorer and a leader of men. He'll be able to write about his expeditions in a way that will be helpful to settlers. Everyone will want to read his reports.

"I've looked for that man a good many years." The Senator sighed. "But I'll find him yet! When people see his maps, they'll feel it's safe to start west."

"Then, when I grow up, I'll travel to the West and make my home there," Jessie cried.

"Sh-h-h, not so loud. Little girls mustn't shout," her father said, but he smiled. At that moment they heard the clock downstairs begin to strike the hour. "It's time I was on my way to Capitol Hill. But you've had lessons in history and geography today, Jessie."

She looked surprised. Then her face fell. "I wish I were going with you."

Senator Benton looked at his daughter and hesitated. "I will take you with me," he said. "Run and tell Miss Emily, and change your shoes. Put on the heavy leather ones you wear at Cherry Grove when we walk in the woods. The thin slippers you have on aren't any good for the unpaved streets of Washington."

"I will, I will!" Jessie cried, and fairly flew.

Capitol Hill

"MISS EMILY! Miss Emily!" Jessie shouted as she ran from the study. "Where are my heavy shoes? Quick! I have to put them on to go with Father. He's going to take me to the Capitol."

"To the Capitol?" said Miss Emily. "You must have misunderstood your father. He wouldn't take you there. You're too young, and a girl at that. And even if you were going, the heavy shoes wouldn't do at all. No lady in Washington wears such ugly things."

"But Father's waiting! He told me to put them on." Jessie was ready to cry.

"In that case," said Miss Emily, beginning to

believe her, "I'll have to find something fit for you to wear."

"There isn't time for me to change my dress," the little girl cried, "only my shoes."

"What! Wear an everyday dress when you're going to the Capitol and sit with Senators and important people? It won't do! Dear me, I really don't know what you should wear." She looked at Jessie's pretty, frilly party dresses. "These won't do, either. I've never heard of a little girl going to the Capitol. We'll have to ask your mother."

Mrs. Benton was surprised when a breathless Jessie told her the news. What would the Senator do with a little girl in the Capitol? He'd hardly take her into the Senate Chamber with him. Would Jessie have to sit quietly for hours in the visitors' gallery?

But Mrs. Benton didn't say a word against Jessie's going. She told Miss Emily she thought the dress her daughter had on was exactly right. "It's warm, and that's important because the halls in the Capitol are drafty. Help her change her shoes, since her father wishes it."

Then she kissed Jessie and told her to run along and be a good girl.

Jessie dashed back to the study where her father was waiting. They went downstairs and out to the street.

She had to run most of the way to the Capitol, for the Senator was a tall man and took long steps. He kept forgetting Jessie had short legs. She skipped and hopped and jumped and ran to keep up with him. As they went along, he talked to her about the men who were in the Congress and what they did.

To himself he was saying, "What shall I do with Jessie when we get there? Where shall I leave her? I can't take her into the Senate with me. It'd be too hard for her to sit still. But she can't wander around alone."

Suddenly he had a happy thought. Jessie liked books, so she would probably be interested in the Congressional Library. He would leave her with Mr. Meehan, the librarian, who was a good friend.

Mr. Meehan looked nervous when Senator Benton led Jessie to him, introduced her, and explained the plan he had in mind.

"But my dear Senator," Mr. Meehan whispered, "this is most unusual, you know! I've no idea how to care for a child this young—especially a little girl. What shall I do if she cries? What if she runs away? I'm not so young as I used to be. I couldn't possibly catch her." He wrung his hands and followed Jessie's father to the door. "How can I amuse her if she gets lonesome for you?"

"You don't need to worry," Senator Benton said encouragingly. "She can take care of herself. Just give her some books with pictures. That will be all she needs."

Mr. Meehan dreaded to turn back into the library. He was sure he'd find Jessie crying. Or worse yet, she'd pull books off the shelves and tear out the pages. That would never do! He trembled at the thought, and hurried back to the little girl.

Then he sighed with relief. She wasn't crying

and hadn't touched a thing. Instead she was looking with interest at the rows of books around the room. "Now, what can I give you to look at?" he asked.

"Do you have any books about French explorers?" Jessie asked. "Father was telling me about some this morning. I'd like to know more about what they did in the West."

Mr. Meehan said he had a few, but he felt they might be a little too hard for her to read. "How would you like to look at bird pictures? I have a whole book of those. They were painted by Mr. Audubon, a friend of your father."

Jessie thought she'd like those. So Mr. Meehan lifted the big book down for her.

They looked about for a place to put it, where she could turn the pages easily. At last Mr. Meehan placed it on a tall bookstand, and Jessie climbed up into one of the big library chairs. Soon she was poring over the pictures.

For a while Mr. Meehan puttered about, keeping an eye on her. He had planned a busy morning, but decided he might as well put everything aside now. "This little girl will soon tire of her book," he thought. "She'll ask a hundred questions and want to get up and down every minute."

But Jessie fooled him. She kept her eyes on the pictures and sounded out words quietly to herself. She didn't ask a single question.

The Congressional Library was a busy place. Men came in all morning long. Some came to look up records of the Congress. Others came with questions about history or laws. There were teachers, lawyers and statesmen asking for books. Mr. Meehan forgot his little guest.

About noon a new visitor came in. He was a tall, slender man with dark blue eyes. "Is that your granddaughter?" he asked Mr. Meehan. "A beautiful, well-behaved child."

"Who? What? Oh, yes! The little girl!" Mr. Meehan remembered with a start. "That's Senator Benton's daughter Jessie." The librarian peered over his glasses at his caller. "Why, it's Mr. Key," he cried with pleasure. Francis Scott Key was a well-known Washington lawyer. Mr. Meehan shook the gentleman's hand several times. Then he chuckled.

"Do you know that little girl has been here all morning? She's been reading Audubon's bird book and hasn't bothered anyone."

Mr. Key looked at Jessie with even more interest. "I've heard President Jackson speak of her," he said. "She must be an unusual girl."

Just then a Senate page came in with a note for Mr. Meehan. It was from Senator Benton. Senator Henry Clay of Kentucky was making an important speech, and Jessie's father could not leave. He suggested that Mr. Meehan send her home with the page.

But Mr. Meehan said he would keep Jessie until Senator Benton came. He sent a note with the page to tell the Senator that Jessie could stay in the library. Then he introduced the little girl to Mr. Key.

Jessie looked up at the tall gentleman. "Oh!" she exclaimed. "You're the one who wrote the song about our flag. My sister and I know all the words. Did you really see the British fleet fire on Fort McHenry?"

Mr. Key smiled and told her the story of the long night, almost twenty years before, when he had written "The Star-Spangled Banner."

Then he looked at the bird book still open on the bookrest before Jessie. "Audubon is a wonderful painter," he said. And he showed Jessie some of the birds he had seen in his own home state of Maryland.

The time passed so quickly Jessie was astonished when her father came at one o'clock.

"You must bring your little daughter often, Senator," Mr. Meehan said. "Let her stay here with me any time. She is more than welcome."

Mr. Meehan wasn't the only one who spoke pleasantly about Jessie. Mr. Key went out of his way to tell her father what a good listener she was. "Bring her to my home someday," he said. "I would like to have my daughter, Alicia, know Jessie."

These kind remarks pleased Senator Benton. He thought about them all the way home. As she skipped and hopped along, Jessie told her father her day's adventures. She described some of the beautiful birds his friend, Mr. Audubon, had painted.

"I don't understand why Miss Emily ever complained about Jessie," Senator Benton said to his wife that night. "She was no trouble at all today." He told her how he had left their daughter at the library and what his friends had said.

"I think I'll take her with me every day. She learns quickly. I can teach her as we come and go, and make lessons out of our walks. I'll see that she gets home at noon, though, so she can take music and dancing lessons with Eliza. I'll hire a special tutor to teach the girls French and history. Miss Emily can teach the younger children their letters, but she can't handle these other subjects."

Soon it was a common sight to see Senator Benton and his lively little companion going up to the Capitol. Some days Jessie stayed in the Congressional Library with Mr. Meehan. Other days she sat in the Senate gallery and listened to the speeches and arguments.

Many women thought Elizabeth Benton was making a mistake when she let her little girl be away from home every morning.

"Tch, tch, tch!" clucked the governess in the house next door. "She'll be a spoiled young one!

Miss Emily tells me Jessie already has her father wrapped around her little finger."

Mrs. Dix, a close neighbor, shook her head doubtfully. "She's a dainty little child now, but she won't be after a while. See what long steps she has to take to keep up with the Senator! Her legs will be stretched. It can't help making her awkward. It's a pity! I almost feel I should say something to Mrs. Benton."

Still another neighbor, Mrs. Key, said, "Think what all that teaching by her father will do to her brain!"

A Senator's Job

MOST mornings, as soon as breakfast was over, Jessie followed her father upstairs to his study. She kept several books piled on her chair, so she wouldn't waste any time climbing to her high seat.

"Now what shall we do today, Father?" she'd ask.

At first he showed her maps. Jessie liked to look at them and copy them. Later Senator Benton gave her history books he thought she could understand.

"I'm going to have a caller this morning, Jessie," he said one day. "You may stay in here if you look at your books quietly. Sound out the words as best you can to yourself. You mustn't interrupt us."

Jessie got down from her high perch and sat on the bearskin rug in front of the fire. Father's caller turned out to be Sam Houston. Jessie immediately forgot her book when the tall Tennessean appeared. He was dressed like an Indian! She stared at him while he and her father talked about their war experiences many years before. Both had served under General Andrew Jackson in the War of 1812.

But Sam Houston had come to talk about Indians, too. He wanted a new treaty for the tribes in the Southwest. Jessie was so interested that she listened to every word.

"The settlers are breaking peace treaties which the government made with the Indians," Sam Houston told her father. "The Indians will live by these agreements if the white man will.

94

But fighting will continue if settlers keep moving onto Indian hunting grounds. The Indians will move farther west—if they may have land that belongs only to them. President Jackson believes I'm right. But I need your help in the Senate, too."

Sam Houston got excited. He paced up and down the room. He hardly noticed the little girl on the floor. Jessie crawled under a table to make sure he wouldn't step on her. She was afraid of

this big man in beaded buckskin clothes and moccasins. The two men talked for a long time.

Jessie could hardly wait to question her father. "Why was Mr. Houston dressed like an Indian?" she asked when the visitor had gone.

"Sam Houston was adopted by the Cherokee Indians when he was a boy," her father answered. "They even gave him a Cherokee name, which means 'The Raven.' But he left them, to fight under Andrew Jackson. Later he was a Congressman and then Governor of Tennessee. Now he's gone back to the Indians. He's living with a Cherokee tribe in the Oklahoma territory. He knows I'm interested in peaceful settlement of the West. I want to try to avoid trouble between the Indians and the whites."

Before Senator Benton could tell her any more, another caller was announced. This time it was Francis Blair. Jessie knew he was the editor of a Washington newspaper.

"Good morning, Tom," he said to Jessie's father. "I want to get a copy of your last speech in the Senate. We want to print it in the *Globe*."

The Senator looked very much pleased. He began to search among the papers on his desk. "I hope the speech did some good. These Easterners just don't understand how important hard money is to the West."

The men went on talking about money and banks. Jessie didn't understand any of this talk. She was bored and picked up her book again.

Before he left, Mr. Blair stopped to speak to her. "How are you this morning, Miss Jessie? I hear you are the newest member of the Senate."

Jessie smiled at this mild-faced man. She didn't mind if Mr. Blair teased her, for she liked him. "I'm just learning how to help my father speak up for the West," she answered.

Both men were delighted with Jessie's reply. "A chip off the old block!" said Mr. Blair. Then he left, with a copy of the Senator's speech in his hand.

"Jessie, I'm afraid we can't talk any more this morning," her father said. "I've lost so much time already that I must finish my own work."

Senator Benton had barely had time to pick up his pen when the third visitor of the day appeared. He was a roughly dressed man who gave his name as Samuel Bates.

"I'm from Missouri," he explained, "and I just want to shake your hand before I go back home."

"I'm glad you stopped by, Mr. Bates," replied the Senator. "I'm always at the service of anyone from our state. How are things in Missouri now? I haven't been home for several months."

"Well, some people are a little worried. They're hoping the public lands will get cheaper so they can buy some. And gold is mighty hard to come by. There's too much paper money, which is not as valuable as gold."

"That's exactly what I've been telling the Congress!" exclaimed Senator Benton. "There are thousands of acres of good farmland going to waste because men can't afford to buy it. They need that land, and the United States needs to have them settle it. We must give more men more opportunity to help build our country."

"Senator Benton, that's what the people of Missouri want to hear! We know you're doing all you can to help us, and we're behind you."

The two men shook hands once more, and the Senator again returned to his desk.

"Father," said Jessie, "I don't see how you ever get your work done. People are always interrupting you."

"They're not interrupting my work," replied her father. "These people are a part of my work—a very important part. Being a Senator means much more than just making speeches and going to meetings on Capitol Hill. I have to talk with many people and listen to their ideas and opinions. The sort of talk you've heard this morning helps me decide how to vote on important matters.

"I need to know what the people back home in Missouri are thinking. And here in Washington I hear many sides of every problem. A Senator needs to have all the information he can get before he can know which bills he should vote for and which bills he should vote against."

"Being a Senator isn't an easy job, is it?" his daughter said.

"No," answered her father, "the job isn't easy. But if we want the United States to become a great country, we can't always take the easiest way."

The White House

"Could you go calling at the White House with me this afternoon, Elizabeth?" Senator Benton asked at the breakfast table one morning. "The President asked me to stop by before we leave Washington."

"Oh, dear, I'm afraid I've packed all my afternoon dresses," Mrs. Benton replied. "We've put everything in trunks except the clothes we'll wear on the trip to Cherry Grove."

"Wear what you have on," her husband suggested. He thought his wife looked beautiful in anything. "This won't be a formal call. We'll take the children. You can visit with Mrs.

Donelson, and the youngsters can play together while the President and I have our talk."

Mrs. Donelson was Andrew Jackson's niece. She acted as hostess at the White House, for his wife, Rachel, had died just before Andrew Jackson became President.

Mrs. Benton was about to say it would be much easier to get out one dress for herself than it would be to find clothes for all five of the children.

Senator Benton didn't guess his wife's thought, and went on talking. "Jackson is a lonely man. He's crusty at times, but he enjoys having children play around him."

"Then we'll all go," kind Mrs. Benton said. "And we'll dress in our best. I wonder which carriage we should use. Do you think it's going to rain?"

"Do you have to decide about the carriage now?" the Senator asked in surprise. "Why can't you wait until this afternoon and see what the weather is?"

"It makes all the difference in what we'll wear," Mrs. Benton explained. "If the sun is shining, most of our friends will be out driving. We should wear our new spring clothes then, and I'd like to use an open carriage. We can stop to speak to people as we pass, and I can see what the ladies are wearing."

Mr. Benton smiled, but his wife was serious. "It means a lot of unpacking," she went on. "But I think I'll have Aunt Nancy and Miss Emily get out two sets of clothes for everybody, one for rain, and one for sunshine."

"Shall I help Aunt Nancy pick out what Eliza and I will need?" Jessie asked. "I'll have plenty of time, because Father and I won't be going to the Capitol." Jessie, now almost nine years old, had a new dress that she had never worn. She could hardly wait to wear it.

"No," said Senator Benton. He believed in keeping his children busy. "All of you must practice your French, so you can talk easily with our old St. Louis friends. We'll go to St. Louis when we leave Cherry Grove."

"I can hardly wait to get there," Jessie cried. "It'll be more fun this year, because I can remember people. Always before I was too little. St. Louis is my favorite home."

"You don't like it better than Cherry Grove, do you?" Eliza asked. She thought there could be no place in the world so wonderful as Grandfather and Grandmother McDowell's plantation in Virginia. "I love the cherry blossoms there, and the roses and honeysuckle, and the green hills and fields. We have so much fun there."

"I like all that, too," Jessie said, "but I still like St. Louis better. I like to see people coming and going on a street, and the boats steaming up and down the Mississippi."

Randy spoke up. "How about the good old Potomac here? Don't you like it? It has lots of boats on it."

"Oh, yes, I like the Potomac. But the Mississippi is so big and exciting. I love to see the boats come in to the levee, and I like to watch passengers get off. There are always all kinds of people—Indians and traders and soldiers and trappers and explorers and——"

"And sometimes," Randy shouted, "we get off. Hurrah for St. Louis!"

"Hurrah!" little two-year-old Mac echoed and clapped his hands.

Jessie continued to think about her new dress. She slipped out of the dining room and begged and pleaded with Aunt Nancy until the old nurse unpacked it. When Miss Emily saw it laid out on the bed, she fretted and scolded. The dress was of fine white cambric, with rows and rows of tiny ruffles. The pantalets that went with it were trimmed with ruffles and lace and narrow velvet bows.

"The dress is entirely too summery," Miss Emily said. "If it rains, you will look funny."

"It isn't going to rain," Jessie said that afternoon as she and Eliza were dressing. She picked up the pretty ruffled things and pranced around the room with them.

"I don't believe you should put those on," Eliza said anxiously. "You'll make Miss Emily cross. And the sky is clouding up again. I see a few drops of rain on the window."

But Jessie's mind was made up. It wasn't going to rain, and she would wear the dress.

When she was ready, Jessie started out to show the dress to her father. Instead, she bumped into Miss Emily. She tried to make the best of things. She spread her skirt and smiled. "How do you like it?"

"I don't like it at all! Not on a day like this."

Miss Emily pressed her lips together. "Why did you put that on? Now you'll have to take it off and dress all over again."

"I want to show it to Father first," Jessie said, keeping out of reach. She skipped out and went to her father, who was in his study.

"Good afternoon, Mr. Senator," she said. She made a low curtsy.

Her father was delighted. He bowed over her hand. "That's a very becoming dress, Miss Jessie," he said, smiling. He was about to add he was glad she was wearing it to the White House.

Just then Mrs. Benton came in. "Oh, Jessie, dear," she cried, "didn't Miss Emily tell you to put on your dark dress? It's going to rain, and it would be a shame to get your lovely new dress soaked the very first time you wear it. Besides, no one would see it, because we're going in the closed carriage.

"Run along and take it off, dear. Don't provoke Miss Emily. She's right about such things."

Jessie walked slowly back to her room and took off the dress. No one but Eliza knew how disappointed she was. "Miss Emily is always right," Jessie said hotly, "and I'm always wrong." The tears spilled down on her dark, rainy-day dress.

Eliza couldn't say much, but she hugged Jessie. She dried her little sister's eyes and spoke so lovingly that Jessie soon felt much better. By the time the girls went downstairs, Jessie was smiling again. And she was as gay as ever during the ride up Pennsylvania Avenue.

At the White House Mrs. Donelson welcomed Mrs. Benton with a glad smile. "I'm so happy that you're the first callers to come," she said. "I always enjoy visiting with you."

President Jackson also welcomed Senator and Mrs. Benton.

In a few minutes he turned to the Senator. "Come to the other end of the room where we can talk, Tom. I want to tell you about a letter I just received from Sam Houston. He's down in Texas now. He says there may be war with Mexico."

When she heard the name Sam Houston, Jessie decided to go with her father and the President. She wanted to hear what "The Raven" had been doing.

Other people began to arrive before the two men had finished talking. Cabinet members and Senators joined them. The women stopped to visit with Mrs. Donelson and Mrs. Benton.

"Is that Mrs. Benton's little girl sitting over there with the men?" one Senator's wife whispered to another. "Isn't it rather odd for her to be there?"

"Oh, no," was the whispered reply. "Our daughters might feel out of place, but Jessie Benton is different. My husband says Senator Benton takes her everywhere with him. She often sits in the gallery of the Senate Chamber and listens to the debates."

Mrs. Benton saw the women whispering together and guessed what they were saying. "It's a good thing we're leaving tomorrow for Virginia," she said to Mrs. Donelson. "It's time

Jessie played more with children her own age. I must remember to tell Thomas there'll be no lessons for her this summer."

In a little while they started home. The sun was shining brightly as they left the White House. Mrs. Benton was almost sorry she'd taken Miss Emily's advice about clothes. Many friends in open carriages nodded as they passed. Some stopped to wish the Bentons a safe journey to Cherry Grove and on to St. Louis. Senator Daniel Webster was one of them.

"That long trip west is dangerous for a woman with so many small children," he said to Mrs. Benton. "I'm always surprised that Senator Benton lets you risk it. Aren't you afraid of Indian attacks on the way? Are you even safe in St. Louis after you get there? That's all savage country, to my way of thinking."

Mrs. Benton laughed heartily, for she knew he was joking, but Jessie was very much disturbed. "I don't like him!" she said, when he had driven off.

Her mother was speechless at this outburst. Her father was astonished. "Why, Jessie," he said, "Daniel Webster is one of our great statesmen. He's the outstanding orator of our time."

"I know who he is, and I don't care," Jessie declared. "He doesn't like the West, and I don't like him." She turned to her brothers and sisters. "He didn't even listen when Father was telling the Senate how important the West was for the United States. I hate him!"

Her father laid one of his big hands over her tight little fist. "You mustn't be angry and hate people who disagree with you. Instead, you must find a way to persuade them that you're right."

"But how can I, if they won't listen?"

"If you know you're right, you'll find a way," he said firmly. "It may take a long time. But if you care enough and try hard enough, you'll find plenty of good people who will believe you."

Jessie looked doubtful.

"Let me tell you a little story," her father went on. "Once, when I first came into the Senate, Mr. Webster was arguing for something he thought was good for the United States. I thought he was wrong, and I did everything I could think of to keep him from getting his way. But he won out.

"Later on, I found that I was wrong and he was right. I was glad then that he hadn't given in, and I went and told him so. We don't always agree, but we respect each other.

"Maybe someday I'll prove to him that I'm right about the West. If I stayed angry and hated him, he'd never listen. He'd pull the other way."

Jessie thought over what her father had said.

"I guess you felt the way I did today about Miss Emily and my new dress. We couldn't agree."

"Only this time you were right, and she was wrong," Eliza said. "The sun is shining, and the dress would have been perfect." But just as she spoke, the sun went under a cloud again.

"I guess we'll have to say she was partly right and partly wrong," Mrs. Benton said. "Because, you see, it's starting to rain again."

The minute the Bentons reached home, Jessie went to Miss Emily. "Thank you for not letting me wear my pretty dress," she said. "You were right. The rain would have spoiled it."

For once, Miss Emily didn't have a scolding word to say.

St. Louis

"I LOVE the hustle and bustle of St. Louis!" Jessie exclaimed.

The Bentons had spent several months at Cherry Grove. Now they had come to Missouri for the rest of the summer. They had just come down the gangplank of the steamboat that had brought them up the Mississippi River. They were standing on the dock.

Jessie looked out over the levee. Along the St. Louis waterfront the riverbank sloped gently toward the shallow water. The bank had been paved, to keep earth from washing down. Small boats could come right up to the levee and un-

116

load their cargo. Larger boats had to tie up at one of the big floating docks, where the water was deeper. Boats and docks were tied up as far as Jessie could see, up and down the levee. Alongside most of them, Negro workers were busy loading or unloading baggage and freight. Overseers were shouting orders in loud voices.

The levee was so crowded with people and freight that Jessie didn't see a single spot where the deck hands could set the Bentons' baggage.

"Almost everyone in town must be here," she said. "There's General William Clark! You wouldn't guess he was a famous explorer, would you? And look, Randy, there's the Governor of Missouri."

Randy didn't answer. He was staring wide-eyed at the crowd. Some of the men wore elegant gold-embroidered velvet clothes. Others were dressed in buckskins. Several Indians were silently watching the activity. Randy could hear some people speaking English and others talking in French or Spanish.

"What's the matter with you, Randy?" asked Jessie. "Can't you say anything?"

Her little brother looked excited. "See the Indians? See all the different people!"

"There are so many things going on at once," Jessie said. "Let's find out what they're unloading over there." She pointed to a big steamboat tied a few yards away. Men were rolling big barrels and little barrels down the gangplank and across the dock. They stacked these on the levee, ready to be carted off. Next they came carrying crates of chickens.

"There's a rooster in a box by himself!" Randy shouted. "See his head poking out?"

"Who do you suppose is getting all those chickens?" Jessie wondered aloud. "Maybe some pioneers who are going farther west. They'll have fresh eggs in their new home."

"They're taking cows, too. And one cow has a calf!" Randy was pointing and yelling in his excitement over everything.

"I don't think they could take cows in a wagon train," Jessie said. "They couldn't get them across rivers. Do you think they could?" she asked a quiet-looking man, who was standing near by.

"Not if they're going far beyond St. Louis," he said pleasantly. "They wouldn't take chickens, either. I expect they'd like to. It would be nice to have fried eggs once in a while, instead of fried mush. But chickens need a lot of grain, and that takes space and costs money. Besides, that rooster there would be sure to crow early some morning."

"I know why that would be bad," Randy said. "Some fierce Indians might hear him. That would give away the camping place!"

Just then there was a commotion near the

gangplank. The little calf was about to wobble overboard. Several men ran up to help steady it. Jessie moved back, out of the way. Without noticing, she backed near the edge of the floating dock. Another half step and she'd go over. She was so interested in what was going on that she didn't even hear her father's warning shout.

He had been searching for the two children. Just as he caught sight of them, he saw Jessie step back, back, back. .

"Stop her, somebody!" he yelled. He pushed frantically through the crowd to get to her. It was like a nightmare. He couldn't reach her. "She'll fall into the deep water," he panted, "and drown before we can save her." He thought of the muddy river.

She was about to step back again. "Look out! Look out, Jessie!" he shouted in despair. The men who were unloading the calf heard

him and saw him pointing. They looked, but
they were too alarmed to move. Jessie saw their
faces turned toward her.

"What's the matter?" she asked. "Did I do
something wrong?" She stepped back again.
Her foot slipped over the edge. She lost her bal-
ance and fell.

"She's going in!" someone screamed.

With a big splash, Jessie went into the muddy
waters of the Mississippi River!

The quiet, pleasant man moved like lightning to the edge of the dock. When Jessie's head bobbed up, he reached out until he could touch her shoulder. Then he caught hold of her dress. His strong arms pulled her safely back, lifted her out of the water and set her on her feet. "Are you all right, little sister?" he asked.

Muddy water streamed from Jessie's hair and clothes. She had swallowed some, too, that nearly strangled her. She choked and gasped for breath. Still frightened, she nodded.

The man smiled. "Don't turn your back on the river the next time," he said. "Always face danger, we say in the West."

By this time the crowd was swarming around her. Senator Benton was there, and General Clark and the Governor, and Grandma's coachman, Gabriel, who had come to meet the boat. A host of bystanders ran up to see why everybody else was running.

"Are you sure you're all right?" her father asked again and again. He couldn't believe Jessie was safe. He held her as if he were afraid she'd vanish. "Who rescued you—and how?"

Jessie pointed to the man who had pulled her from the river. "He did. One second I was falling, the next second I was in the river, and the second after that he had pulled me out."

The man introduced himself as a fur trapper. Senator Benton thanked him again and again. "Right now I must take my daughter home where she can get into dry clothes," he said. "But I wish you'd come to the house later. I want to talk to you some more." The Senator took Jessie and Randy by the hands and led them back to the family.

None of the family had seen what happened. They couldn't imagine what had kept Senator Benton so long. Gabriel had already loaded all their baggage in the carriage. There was a great

to-do when they saw Jessie in her dripping clothes. After the Senator had told them about the accident, everybody had to hug Jessie and give thanks that she was safe. At last they were ready to start for Grandma's.

It was only a short distance, but they were going on horseback. The streets were too dusty for the ladies to walk. Their skirts would be ruined. After everyone was mounted, they moved off in a long parade. Aunt Nancy and the two youngest children rode in the carriage with Gabriel.

Miss Emily meant to take Jessie aside and give her a good lecture for wandering off and causing her father such worry. "You're nine years old and ought to know better," she was going to say. But the governess was having troubles of her own. She didn't like to ride horseback, and every horse she rode knew it. This one jolted her up and down and bounced her to and fro, so she couldn't get a word out straight. The scolding turned into a stammer.

"Je-Je-Je-Je-Jessie—I-I-I-I—wa-wa-want y-y-y-you t-t-t-to——"

"I beg your pardon, Miss Emily?" Jessie asked politely.

The governess tried again, but the words wouldn't come out. She shut her lips and shook her head.

By this time Jessie had recovered from her fright. She enjoyed the ride in spite of her wet clothes, for the summer day was quite warm. She rode up beside Eliza and her parents. "I could tell where I am right now, even if I couldn't see or hear," she said suddenly. "Can you guess how?"

"No, I'm sure I can't," said Eliza.

"Shut your eyes and guess."

"I know," Senator Benton said. "You can tell by the *plop-plop-plop* of the horses' hoofs."

No, that wasn't it. "Remember," Jessie reminded him, "you're not supposed to be able to hear, either."

"I know," her mother said. "By the smell of the locust blossoms."

"Yes!" Jessie cried. "I always think of this street and of Grandma's yard when I smell the locust trees."

"Hey, don't shut your eyes now," Randy called from the head of the line. "We're almost there. I see Grandma on the porch!"

Senator Benton couldn't hold back any longer. He spurred his horse ahead. He waved his hat and called in a deep, glad voice, "We're here, Mother! All of us are home at last!" He leaped from his horse and gathered the old lady in his arms.

Then all the children lined up on the step and took their turns kissing Grandma and telling her their names. She couldn't keep track of all her grandchildren. They grew too fast between visits. And now there was the new baby, Susan, who had been born at Cherry Grove.

When Grandma saw Jessie's wet clothes, she wanted to hear all about the accident. After she had heard what happened, she gave Jessie an extra kiss.

Miss Emily whisked Jessie off to change her clothes. The others stayed downstairs. By the time they all had welcomed one another and caught up on the family news, it was time for lunch. Neighbors began to call before lunch was over. Soon the house was full of company. Even the porch and the yard were full.

Miss Emily took the children upstairs for a little rest. Eliza was glad to stretch out, but Jessie wanted to be down with the grownups. So she did the next best thing.

On the second floor of Grandma's house were wide balconies that ran the length of the house.

Each upstairs room had a door that opened onto a balcony. Jessie loved to lean on the railing and look down on company.

Jessie slipped out of her room to the edge of the balcony. She saw her father sitting almost directly beneath her. A group of men had drawn their chairs in a circle around him. One man was talking, and the rest were listening to every word. Jessie tried to make out what he was saying, but someone kept making a *psst-psst-psst* sound. It drowned out the words.

"I wish whoever is hissing would hush," she grumbled. Then, suddenly, she realized it was someone close by and looked around. There was Randy, hissing as hard as he could.

"Come here." He beckoned. "Do you know who that man with red hair is?" He pointed to the speaker.

Jessie leaned over and saw the man's face for the first time. "Of course I know him," she answered importantly. "That's General William Clark. I tried to tell you about him this morning, but you wouldn't listen."

"Tell me now. Please, Jessie," begged Randy.

"Father told me all about General Clark one day when we were talking about the West. Thirty years ago the United States bought all

130

the land west of the Mississippi River from France. No one knew much about it. President Jefferson decided to send an expedition to explore the country. Meriwether Lewis was one of the leaders and William Clark was the other."

"How far west did they go?" asked Randy.

"All the way to the Pacific Ocean. They were the very first white men to cross America, north of Mexico. They made the first maps of this country. They had to cross very high mountains and go through country where hostile Indians lived.

"When they got back, General Clark went to his home in Virginia. But he liked the West so well he came out to St. Louis to live. Now he's Superintendent of Indian Affairs in Missouri."

"Look! Look!" said Randy. "There's the man who pulled you out of the river! He just got here. He's talking to Father."

"Let's go down and listen," Jessie whispered.

"All right," agreed Randy.

The children hurried downstairs and out onto the porch. Then they stopped.

"Aw!" Randy exclaimed. "They're all leaving!"

"Why did they have to go now?" Jessie wailed. "That's just our luck."

The party was certainly breaking up. Mother was coming upstairs to rest before supper. Father was standing in the yard telling the riders good-by. Randy and Jessie watched them go.

The Senator turned and came up on the porch. Jessie ran to him. "Oh, Father, I wanted to thank that nice man for saving my life. I was so scared this morning that I forgot."

"I'm sorry, Jessie," her father replied. "I thought you were asleep. He could stay only a minute because he's leaving this afternoon to join Jim Bridger. They're going on a trapping expedition. He knows how grateful we are."

132

"Father, it seems funny we couldn't tell by looking at him that he's a trapper. I thought they were all big, rough, wild-looking men. This morning he was just standing there watching. And he was so gentle."

"But when the time came to do something, he did it," the Senator said. "Faster than anybody else could do it, too. He was alert and strong and he thought very quickly. That's important for a mountain man.

"There are a lot of good men like him out here in the West. They're the ones who will blaze the trails that wagon trains will follow."

"And I'm going to see that great West one day!" Jessie said.

The rest of the summer wasn't nearly so exciting as the first day. The weather turned sultry. Everybody was hot and uncomfortable. The baby, Susan, only a few months old, broke out with prickly heat and cried all the time. The little girls whined because Miss Emily made them stay in the house so much. She said they couldn't stand the heat.

Even Grandma was upset. "It isn't healthful for the weather to be so hot this early in the summer," she said anxiously. "That almost always means sickness and fever. We mustn't let the children go near the river. The air there is like steam. That's where plagues start."

Mrs. Benton followed Grandma's advice. It was a good thing she did, because a few days later Gabriel came running to the house. His eyes were wide with fright.

"There's bad news on the levee," he panted. "One of the crew on a boat from New Orleans died of cholera this morning. There's no telling how many others have it."

Mrs. Benton and Grandma grew pale. Cholera was the disease they dreaded most. Very few people ever recovered from it.

"This means that no one is to set foot outside this yard before frost," Grandma said firmly. "No one will come in, either."

"It won't seem like St. Louis if we can't visit with the neighbors or if folks aren't dropping in all day," sighed Elizabeth Benton.

Many people died of cholera that summer. Grandma didn't take any chances with the children. There were no visits to Jefferson Barracks, no boat rides on the river, no trips to the Indian mounds down near Cape Girardeau.

It would have been tiresome for the children if it hadn't been for Grandma. She told them stories of pioneer days in Tennessee, when she first moved there. She told them of the difficulties of clearing land and building houses in the wilderness.

Randy made her tell over and over the stories about Indians in Tennessee. Grandma Benton's house had been twenty-five miles from Nashville. It was only a few hundred paces from the Natchez Trace. This trail was the main pathway for the Indians of the region. Many hunters used it.

White men came up the trail, too. They would take flatboats loaded with goods down smaller rivers to the great Mississippi and on to New Orleans. Then they would travel back up the Natchez Trace. Usually they were carrying the money they had received for their goods. They

had to be careful because robbers hid in dark places on the trail.

On the days Grandma was too tired to tell stories, she let the children go into the library and choose the books they wanted to look at. Jessie was the one who enjoyed those days most. She loved to read. Her mother was worried about her.

"Jessie reads too much," she told Grandma. "All winter she studies with her father. I was hoping she could play like other little girls this summer. And now she has to stay indoors because of the cholera."

"It's a good thing Jessie loves books," Grandma said. "Who knows? She may someday live where there are very few people. Books are a comfort to anyone who is lonely."

The long summer finally came to a close. Frost was in the air and it was safe to start east. The baggage was loaded into the carriage.

The Bentons, in a long line, set out on horse-back for the levee. The children waved to Grandma as long as the house was in sight.

Jessie cried a little. "I hate to tell anyone good-by," she said. "It always makes me sad. Saying good-by to someone you love is the worst thing in the world!"

Cherry Grove

GRANDMOTHER and Grandfather McDowell were expecting the Bentons to arrive at Cherry Grove any minute. Many friends and relatives were also waiting to welcome them.

"I wonder why they're so late," Grandmother said anxiously. "They should be here by now. They were to take the stagecoach to Fredericksburg. We sent the Pumpkin and some saddle horses up there to meet them over a week ago. It's never taken them this long." The Pumpkin was the big, bright-yellow family coach.

"I do hope they haven't had an accident," Cousin Mattie said dolefully. She was a rather sour old lady, who looked on the dark side of everything.

"Now stop worrying," replied Aunt Susan. "Fredericksburg is a hundred and fifty miles away. Many delays can occur on such a long journey. Besides, we'd have heard if there was trouble. Bad news travels fast, you know."

"Not always." Cousin Mattie's voice was dismal. "Remember the time their coach overturned between St. Louis and Washington? Tom's head was cut open. We didn't hear about that for weeks."

Grandmother was more anxious than ever. "I hope nothing like that has happened now," she cried, wringing her hands. "Elizabeth hasn't been well all winter, and little Mac is very frail. I hope the summer here in the country will improve his health." She looked worried.

"What's the matter with little Mac?" asked Aunt Susan anxiously.

140

"Elizabeth wrote me a very sad letter," Grandmother explained. "She says Mac may not live through the summer. He's never been strong."

Just then Grandfather gave a shout. "There they are! I see a cloud of dust on the orchard road." He left the window where he had been watching and moved quickly outside to his horse. The animal had been saddled and waiting, for Grandfather always rode out to meet the coach. Several of the boy cousins went, too.

Everyone else came out on the porch. "I'm so glad they're here at last," said Grandmother with a sigh of relief. "It always seems years between their visits. Cherry Grove is so much livelier when Elizabeth's children are here."

"I should think it would be!" said Cousin Mattie. "That Jessie is so full of energy. She's always climbing trees, even in her best dresses and pantalets. It's a shame she wasn't a boy."

"Why, Mattie, that's no way to talk!" Aunt Susan said. "She's the beauty of the family. It would be a shame if those shining curls and that lovely complexion were wasted on a boy."

"They're wasted, anyway," Cousin Mattie replied. "Don't you remember the time she cut off her curls and went around looking like a plucked chicken?"

"Now, now, Mattie," Grandmother broke in pleasantly. "Jessie was only a little girl then. You'll see a big difference in her this year, I'm

142

sure. She's ten years old now, almost a young lady."

Glad shouts told them the group was near the gate. Grandmother ran down the front steps to be the first to welcome them. The others gathered behind her. The servants crowded around the front door.

Jessie and her cousins were racing their horses. They pulled up at the gate in a cloud of dust. "We're here, Grandmother!" Jessie cried. She jumped down and ran to the open arms of the loving old lady.

Grandmother didn't notice the dust. She saw only that her granddaughter was lovable, happy, and prettier than ever.

Next to appear was Grandfather with Randy on the saddle in front of him. They were followed by the Pumpkin. Eliza and Sarah jumped out, followed by Mrs. Benton and Mac. Miss Emily handed baby Susan to Cousin Mattie.

The Bentons crowded around Grandmother. She was so glad to see them all safe and sound that she was laughing and crying at the same time. "Everything's going to be all right now," she said. "Little Mac will grow stronger here in the fresh air and sunshine. And I know Elizabeth will feel better away from the city. It's going to be the happiest summer we ever had together."

The next morning Jessie was awake before daylight. She wished she could get up, and that people didn't waste so much time sleeping. She hated to lose a minute at Cherry Grove!

She began to think about all she planned to do this summer. "I can explore that section of woods where I've never been before. Father will take me up there, I know. And I hope Grandmother will teach me some more about running a house. I'll follow her around and see what's in all the storerooms. Maybe she'll let me carry the bunch of keys. And I want to ride a lot, because I don't have a horse in Washington.

"But right now I want today to begin!" she thought. "We're going to give out the gifts, and that's always exciting."

Senator and Mrs. Benton always brought a present for everyone on the plantation. Jessie loved to visit all the servants' cabins and give them their gifts. Just thinking about it was fun, but she wished Eliza were awake. Then they could talk about the day ahead.

Finally Jessie could be quiet no longer. She hopped out of her bed and jumped into Eliza's.

"Who is it? What's the matter?" Eliza awoke with a start. "Oh, it's you! Why are you up so early?"

"Don't you remember?" Jessie whispered. "It's the day we give presents to everybody."

Eliza was wide awake now. She enjoyed this day, too. The girls giggled and talked together until Miss Emily came to tell them it was time to get up.

Breakfast at Cherry Grove wasn't like breakfast at home. There were lots of rich foods on the table, things like pies and hot biscuits, besides ham, chicken, cold beef, eggs, and all kinds of jams and jellies. The Bentons were used to plain, simple fare. But the big difference was that everyone didn't sit down at the table at one time. They came whenever they were ready.

The children were the first ones at breakfast this morning. They had lots of fun until at last Miss Emily appeared. She was carrying baby Susan in her arms and leading Mac by the hand. "Your mother isn't well enough to visit the servants' cabins this morning, but we're to go ahead as usual. I'm to have charge."

The children's faces fell.

"It won't be the same without Mother," Jessie protested in disappointment.

"There's no use sulking," said Miss Emily. "The presents are already in the baskets. We can't dilly-dally. I'm taking baby Susan along, and we must remember that Mac mustn't get too much sun, either."

"Oh, we didn't know Susan and Mac were going, too," Jessie cried joyously. And the others joined in, "That's different!" "We'll all hurry." "All the servants will be so happy to see them."

Everyone cheered up. They all loved the two youngest children and were very proud of them. They wanted to show them off.

The children set out in gay spirits. They chattered happily as they followed the road to the servants' cabins. At each cabin they stopped and visited for a few minutes.

Aunt Chloe was a special favorite of the children. She was in charge of the dairy, but she never told on them when they slipped in for some cool milk. This morning she insisted on letting little Mac rest on her lap. She said he was the nicest little boy she'd ever seen.

When they reached Sam's cabin, he took them out to a field to see the new bull. Grandfather McDowell had had the animal shipped all the way from England to Virginia.

"He must be the biggest, strongest bull in the world," said Randy. "Listen to him roar!"

All the children were a little frightened. They backed away from the fence.

"I'll never go into that field!" Sarah declared. "Not even for wild strawberries."

"Grandfather says if you don't run from an animal, it won't hurt you," said Jessie. "He says to look it steadily in the eyes and back away very slowly."

"I still wouldn't want to try it," Randy replied.

They went on to see Aunt Bek. She loved the pretty cups and saucers they had brought her. "Why don't you let me fix you some tea?" she asked.

Miss Emily thanked her. "Mac looks very tired. We've kept him out in the sun much too long already. We really must be getting back to the house."

"It's been wonderful," said Jessie. "With such a good beginning, I know this summer will be the best we've ever spent here."

Jessie Becomes
a Lady

"MY DEAR, we must have a serious talk about Jessie," Mrs. Benton said to her husband one morning.

The Senator looked at her in surprise. A "talk about Jessie" had not been necessary for a long time.

"She's grown up and getting prettier every day. Many girls her age are already going to large balls and receptions. I think girls should be a little older before they go into society. I want Eliza and Jessie to wait until they're seventeen.

"In many ways Jessie seems older than she is.

That's because she has spent so much time with you. She's used to being with grownups. But she still has a lot to learn about living with girls her own age."

Senator Benton thought over his wife's words. "What do you suggest we do?"

"I think we should send Eliza and Jessie to a boarding school. I've talked with some of our friends about different schools. Most of them send their daughters to Miss English's Female Seminary in Georgetown. It's an excellent school, and not too far away."

She waited to hear what her husband would say to this, but he was silent. All he could think about was how much he would miss his favorite daughter.

"Jessie and I have spent so much time together," he was thinking. "I've liked teaching her things, and we've enjoyed learning new things together. In the last few years she's written out my speeches as I dictated them. She has taken notes for me in the Senate. I can't give her up. No one can fill her place." He remembered their walks to and from the Capitol and all the good times they had shared.

At last he spoke. "You're right, of course, Elizabeth. I've been selfish to keep Jessie with me all this time. We'll send her with Eliza to Miss English's, if you think best."

So it was decided. The two sisters were to live at the seminary in Georgetown. Everyone approved of the plan—except Jessie. She was happy at home. Why should she go away to school?

Eliza soon discovered she enjoyed the life at the school. But Jessie was homesick and the lessons bored her.

"The teachers don't make history or literature or anything else interesting, as Father did," she stormed. "They don't try to help you understand the books. They just want you to memorize names and dates.

" I don't like Miss English, either," she fumed to Eliza. "She isn't what I call a real lady. Have you noticed how she smirks and bows to the girls whose fathers are important? She goes past the others with her nose in the air."

Eliza was upset to hear Jessie talk this way. She liked the quiet classrooms and the easy lessons. The piano lessons were especially nice. "Don't you like anything here?" she asked. She was close to tears.

Jessie was sorry she had upset her sister. She decided to keep her troubles to herself after this. But some days it was hard to be cheerful. Spring days were the worst of all.

One pretty April morning, when Jessie was supposed to be studying, she stood looking out the window of her room. She decided she'd run away from school. A big apple tree grew close to the building, and its branches rubbed against the wall. "I'll crawl onto a limb of that tree and climb down to the ground. Then I'll slip out the garden gate. I'll be home before anyone misses me."

She raised the window and was about to step out over the sill when a movement in the tree stopped her. Something alive was out there. It was too big for a squirrel or a cat. The whole limb trembled under its weight. Could it be a prowler? Jessie peered through the leaves. It was a person! But it wasn't a prowler. It was Eleanora Calvert, the girl whose room was next to hers. Jessie had always liked Eleanora, but thought her rather proper. Now she stared at her in surprise.

Eleanora giggled. "Come on out," she whispered. "It's lovely here."

"I thought I was the only girl in the world who climbed trees," Jessie said, as she crawled

154

out and sat down beside her friend. "At least my aunts think so."

"Do you have aunts who try to make a lady of you, too?" Eleanora asked with a sigh.

With that, both of them started to talk. They told each other about their aunts and uncles, their first cousins and second cousins, and their sisters and brothers. Jessie began to tell about her baby brother, Mac, who had died several years ago, and about Randy, who wanted to be an explorer.

Suddenly, they were startled to hear Miss English's voice close beside them. They nearly stopped breathing. Then they saw that the principal was standing by an open window in Harriet Williams' room. Harriet was the pupil whose room was on the other side of Eleanora's. Miss English had her back to the window and didn't see the two girls. They didn't mean to eavesdrop, but they couldn't help hearing.

"Let me see the dress you plan to wear for the recital this afternoon, Miss Williams," Miss English was saying.

"I'm going to wear my blue silk," Harriet replied. "I've worn it often, but it's the only dress I have that's long enough."

"But it won't do!" Miss English cried. "I told you to have your mother send another. The blue dress is too small for you. Besides, it's been turned and faced, and it's shabby."

"The trouble is I grow too fast," Harriet said cheerfully. "There are seven of us at home, you know, and Mother can't keep up with me. We can't afford a seamstress very often. I didn't tell Mother I needed an afternoon dress. I knew she'd go without something for herself if I did."

"Then I'll have to ask you to stay upstairs whenever we have guests," Miss English said coldly, "until you have something suitable to wear in public."

"You mean I'm not to sing in the recital to-day?"

"That is precisely what I mean," the principal replied. "I expect important visitors this afternoon. I pride myself on the genteel appearance of my young ladies. If you appeared as one of my star pupils in this dress, it might cause talk."

"Yes, ma'am," Harriet murmured. There was the sound of a door closing. Then the principal was gone.

"The mean old thing," Jessie muttered.

"Oh! Oh! Harriet must feel awful." Eleanora nearly wept.

"She has the nicest voice of anyone in school," Jessie added. "And her blue dress isn't so bad. It's very becoming, even if it is old."

They sat there feeling sorry. It didn't make them feel any better when they thought they heard Harriet crying.

"I wish we could think of some way to get

even with Miss English," Eleanora said angrily to Jessie.

"Oh, I know!" Jessie cried suddenly. "May Day will be here soon, and we're to vote for a May Queen. Let's get all the girls to vote for Harriet. We'll make her May Queen!"

Eleanora rocked back and forth with glee at the thought. "I'm sure we can do it! Everyone likes Harriet. She's so jolly and friendly. Won't it be fun to see her face when she's chosen?"

"Won't it be fun to see Miss English's?" Jessie laughed.

She forgot about her homesickness in the next few days. She and Eleanora had to talk to a lot of girls. They worked quietly and earnestly. The other pupils joined in the scheme. When the girls voted, Jessie was sure everyone she had talked to had voted for Harriet.

On the day the principal was to announce the name of the queen, every girl was in her seat early. The hall clock chimed. Many of the girls couldn't take their eyes off Harriet.

Miss English rose and cleared her throat. "Young ladies," she began, "your principal and your teachers wish to announce the name of your May Queen—one whom we consider worthy of the honor and a credit to the school—*Miss Mildred Fitzhugh!*"

There was a gasp of amazement, but no one moved or said anything. Mildred looked as if she had been turned to stone.

Then Jessie rose, her cheeks fiery red and her eyes blazing. "This isn't right!" she cried. "It isn't honest, and you know it isn't. We elected Harriet Williams."

Miss English's eyes were shiny black with anger. "I think you must be delirious, Miss Jessie. You may go to your room at once and stay there the rest of the day. I shall send you a tonic that will bring down your fever."

160

Jessie stalked from the room with her head high.

Eliza slipped quietly out of the room, too. This disturbed Miss English more than Jessie's outburst. She was fond of Jessie's gentle sister.

Everyone was glum. The next morning Mrs. Williams came and took her daughter out of school. Jessie cried and cried over that.

When May Day came, the exercises seemed flat. Miss English acted as if nothing had happened. She even hinted that she was pleased Harriet had left the school.

A short time later, though, the principal was sorry. Excited whispers were racing through the classrooms. "Have you heard the news about Harriet? She's to be married to Count Alexander de la Bodisco, the Minister from Russia!"

At noon Jessie cried happily, "Just think—Harriet will be a countess!"

"Isn't it wonderful?" Eleanora sang for joy.

"She'll have everything she wants. The Count is terrifically wealthy."

"I wonder what Miss English is thinking now!" Jessie's eyes danced. "The wedding is to be here in Georgetown, in Harriet's home, but it will be a grand affair. Father says President Van Buren will be there, and all the diplomats. Army and Navy officers will come in their dress uniforms. The ladies will wear their finest silks and satins. It will be the most important social event of the year. I wish we could peek in on it." Both girls sighed wistfully.

Miss English sighed, too. She'd give a good deal to live over that May Day. What a chance she had missed! One of the seminary's own pupils was to marry a count, and Miss English wouldn't be invited to the ceremony. People would raise their eyebrows and wonder why.

One more blow was to come to Miss English. A few days later the Count's white coach, drawn by four prancing black horses, drove up to the school. One of the Count's servants jumped down. He presented an envelope, sealed with the Count's own seal, to the startled maid who answered his knock.

Miss English's heart rose. This was an invitation to the wedding, without a doubt! Her hand trembled as she reached for the envelope.

"It's—it's for Miss Jessie," the maid stammered. "The footman said, 'For Miss Jessie Anne Benton.'"

The maid was right. The writing was bold and clear.

Later Jessie was called to the principal's study. Miss English asked about the envelope. Jessie told her it contained a happy note from Harriet. She wrote that both the Count and the bride wished Jessie to be the maid of honor at their wedding.

When the great day finally came, a large

crowd gathered outside the Williams house in Georgetown. The townspeople wanted to see the important men and women who stepped out of their elegant coaches at the door.

It was a splendid wedding. Foreign diplomats in their court dress of scarlet and gold set off the shimmering white gowns of the bride and the bridesmaids.

Harriet looked beautiful. She wore a coronet

of diamonds on her golden hair, and there were diamonds in her necklace and earrings. These were gifts from the Count. Her dress was of white satin, and her veil of delicate lace hung almost to the end of her long train.

No one would have recognized the maid of honor as the girl who liked to climb trees. Jessie's dress was made of brocaded silk and was almost as gorgeous as Harriet's. She wore a wreath of white rosebuds in her hair and carried a bouquet of white camellias. Some people thought she was lovelier than the bride.

The wedding, and the reception that was held at the Count's residence, and the dinner and reception at the White House several days later were talked about for weeks afterward. Jessie enjoyed every minute of the parties.

When the excitement was over, Jessie went to her parents. "I want to leave the seminary," she announced to them.

"Why, we thought you were happy there," said her mother. They were astonished when she told them how miserable she'd been. Then she told the whole story of the snobbish Miss English.

"On top of all that," she ended, "she has been telling her friends that Harriet, 'our dear Countess, was one of my most beloved pupils.' What do you think of that? You don't want me to study under such a deceitful person, do you?"

She expected her parents to say, "No, of course not!" But they didn't. They thought over her story.

"I believe you should stay at the school a bit longer," her mother said at last. "I don't approve of the way Miss English acted. But you'll find, wherever you go in the world, some people who are like her. You won't get away from them by leaving the seminary. Besides, even though you don't admire Miss English, she has a good

166

school. She watches over her girls carefully and teaches them how to behave like ladies in any company. And you're meeting many nice girls your own age."

"Your mother is right about that," the Senator added. "And you're learning something much more important. That is, to think for yourself, and to stand up for what you think is right. That's a lesson I hope you'll remember all your life."

"You taught me that yourself," Jessie said. "I didn't learn it from Miss English."

"But you are learning how to put it in practice in her school," the Senator reminded her. "It's easier to do that among friends than to try to do it after you're grown."

So Jessie went back to the seminary. Though she never liked the school very well, she liked making new friends, and she even learned how to get along with Miss English.

The Right Man Comes Along

By the time Jessie was seventeen, she was one of the most beautiful and popular young ladies in Washington. One November day of that year, 1841, she was the main topic of Washington gossip.

"Have you heard the news about Jessie Benton?" Mrs. Smith asked her friend, Mrs. Trent. "She eloped with a young Army officer and didn't tell her family. His name is John Charles Frémont."

"I can't believe it!" Mrs. Trent gasped. "I thought she was going to marry a young man who is a West Point cadet."

"Her parents wanted her to marry the West Point cadet. But Jessie has a mind of her own."

"What did Senator Benton say?" Mrs. Trent was all ears.

"He was furious at first, I hear." Mrs. Smith had been busy all morning getting the details. "He ordered Lieutenant Frémont out of the house and out of his sight forever. But he cooled off quickly enough when Jessie started to leave, too. Now he's even asked the young couple to live there at the family home on C Street. Mrs. Benton has given them several nice rooms.

"It's a good thing Jessie's parents forgave her," Mrs. Smith chattered on. "Young Frémont hasn't any money or any background, either."

Mrs. Trent was shocked. "Think of it! Jessie married to a poor nobody."

"Oh, I didn't mean that Lieutenant Frémont is a nobody," her friend interrupted quickly. "Dear me! That French explorer, Nicholas

Nicollet, praises him all the time. The Lieutenant went on the last expedition with Mr. Nicollet. They both are explorers and mapmakers for the government. Lieutenant Frémont has already made a name for himself in the Army. Many people think he'll be famous someday."

"If he's such a great fellow, why did Jessie have to marry him secretly? I thought Senator Benton was interested in explorers."

"He is. And he really likes Lieutenant Frémont. I guess he thought Jessie wouldn't be happy if her husband was always off exploring. It will be a lonely life for her."

"Perhaps Jessie will ask the Senator to arrange a transfer for his son-in-law," Mrs. Trent said, "to some other branch of the service. Someone else could do the exploring."

"I hadn't thought of that! I'll wager Jessie will want her husband to stay at home now."

A few months later the gossips learned they

were mistaken about Jessie's wishes. The government was sending an expedition to explore the country between the Missouri frontier and the Rocky Mountains. Mr. Nicollet was supposed to head the party, but he was ill. He suggested that Lieutenant Frémont take his place. It was a big promotion for the young officer. This was one of the most important expeditions to start west, because much of this territory was still unknown. These explorers were to collect information for the first maps of this part of America.

"Is Jessie trying to keep her husband from going so far away?" Mrs. Trent asked.

"No, indeed," Mrs. Smith replied. "Jessie and her father are both helping him. They've introduced him to important people and have roused public interest in the expedition. The Senator is even letting his son, Randy, go along."

"The Frémonts are a popular couple," said

Mrs. Trent. "They're being entertained everywhere. Everyone was congratulating them at
President Tyler's reception."

"It was a lucky day for Lieutenant Frémont
when he married Jessie."

AN EXPLORER'S WIFE

Lieutenant Frémont left home in May. He
was gone almost six months. These were long,
lonely months for Jessie. She kept busy in the
daytime. Mrs. Benton was very ill and Jessie
was both nurse and housekeeper. She helped
her father with his speeches again, too, and she
took long walks.

The nights were the hardest. Jessie knew that
brave, alert, experienced scouts like Kit Carson
were with her husband. But she kept imagining
all kinds of terrible things that might happen to
him. She imagined him freezing to death in the

172

mountains, or starving on the desert, or captured by hostile Indians. The months seemed like years.

But at last the Lieutenant returned. He was thin and sunburned, but happy and successful. Jessie was joyful. She forgot her hours of loneliness.

Two weeks after her husband arrived home, Jessie had another reason to be joyful. The Frémonts' first child was born. They named the little girl Elizabeth, for Jessie's mother.

Mr. Nicollet was pleased when he saw Lieutenant Frémont's maps. He declared they were the best maps of the West that had been drawn. "They mark clearly the trail across the country to the Rocky Mountains," he said.

Jessie wanted to know all about the expedition. She studied the maps, and her husband told her all that had happened along the way. He pointed to one large, open space. "It was here that we saw our first buffalo herd. We were out of fresh meat, so we decided to halt for a day and hunt buffalo. My, how we feasted that night!

"But usually we had only small fires after dark," he added. "There were said to be savage Indians in that territory. Most of the tribes we met, however, were friendly or only curious.

"Most important, though, we found a lot of good farmland. And we marked the best ways to reach it. There is plenty of farmland for every settler who wants to go west. We collected a lot of information about water, soil, wildlife, temperature, and weather."

"That will be important to settlers," Jessie said. "Hurry and write out your report so copies can be printed. I know people will be more eager to start west when they find you have charted the way."

Lieutenant Frémont shut himself in his room

and went to work on his report. After a few days he came to Jessie. He looked glum. "I've filled a wastebasket with wrong beginnings," he said. "When I try to write it down, it all sounds dull. No one will read the report."

Jessie was rocking their little month-old daughter Elizabeth. Now she laid the baby in the cradle and led her explorer-husband into the library. She sat down at the desk where she had done work for the Senator while her husband

was away. She laid out her pens, paper and ink. Then she looked up at him. "Now begin at the beginning. Tell me the whole adventure just as you did when you were explaining your maps. When you talked it sounded exciting."

Telling his experiences to Jessie was different. Lieutenant Frémont talked, and his wife took notes. She knew just what questions to ask to keep him talking, and the right words came easily in his answers.

Every morning they went to work. He dictated until noon. In the afternoon she wrote out her notes and went over them with him. It took them several months to finish the report, but working together was fun.

Senator Benton read it first. "This tells people what they want to know. The report is interesting and practical," he said. "It's exactly what we want." He took the report to both the Senate and the House of Representatives.

The Congress was pleased with the report and had a thousand copies printed at once. These were gone very quickly. Many newspapers published it as a serial. Soon the whole country was reading about and talking about the Frémont expedition to the West.

Farmers talked about the fertile prairies beyond Missouri. They were interested in this land where they could have their own farms and raise big crops. "Let's move out west," they said to their wives. "John Frémont's report tells us what to expect, and his maps will help us get there."

"Yes," the women agreed, "let's raise our families where we can build our own homes."

Soon large wagon trains began the long trip west. The tracks of their wheels left a trail across the plains so recently crossed by Frémont.

The Golden West

Jessie hoped the Army would let her husband stay in Washington for a while. But his expedition had been so successful that the Congress soon ordered him to lead another. This time he was to follow the Oregon Trail.

It was more than a year before Lieutenant Frémont returned. Almost as soon as he had greeted his wife, he announced, "Jessie, I've come back with great batches of notes. I'll need your help even more on my second report."

"It will be fun to work on it together," she said happily. "We'll make this report even better than the first one was!"

The Congress thought the second report was better, and it ordered five thousand extra copies printed. Again John Charles Frémont's work was admired and praised. Jessie was very proud when the Army promoted him to captain. And now the government wanted him to seek an easier route to the West Coast.

This time Captain Frémont led his men farther south, around the Great Salt Lake and across the desert. Then they crossed the mountains and entered California. It had always been a province of Mexico, but recently many Americans had been allowed to settle there. Captain Frémont hoped to find a good route through California valleys, up the coast to Oregon.

But he couldn't carry out his plan. Before his party could leave the province, the United States and Mexico declared war. For some time the two countries had been quarreling with each other over border settlements.

John Charles Frémont had always believed that California ought to belong to the United States, because of its location. He and Jessie and Senator Benton had all dreamed of one great nation, stretching from ocean to ocean. Now Frémont saw a chance to help win California for his country. He and his men joined the settlers in fighting against Mexican troops.

Two years passed before Jessie saw her husband again. After the fighting was over, he returned home and resigned from the Army.

Meanwhile, his maps and the reports had been studied and read all over the world. Many honors came to him. Not a word was said about his wife, but Jessie didn't expect praise. It was enough for her to know that she had helped tell the people about the West and that many more settlers were finding the way there.

Jessie and her husband had made plans to go west and settle in California. But then a railroad company asked John to make one more expedition, to find a good pass for a railroad through the Rocky Mountains.

"This is to be my last journey to the West without you," he told Jessie. They had been married seven years. Lily, as they called their little daughter, was six years old. John had been in the West most of those years.

"I'll find the pass for the railroad. Then I'll go on to San Francisco," John said. "You and Lily meet me there. I've bought a ranch near the coast for us. I'll wait for you."

Jessie wanted to go overland, but everyone made a fuss about the long, hard journey.

"Very well," she said at last, "I'll go by boat."

CALIFORNIA AT LAST

Jessie and Lily set out from New York, happy and excited about their trip.

182

When they reached Panama, they had been told, they would have to leave their ship and travel by horseback across the Isthmus of Panama. From here, boats would take them up the coast to California.

The first part of the trip went well. But bad luck awaited them at Panama. Fever was raging all through the country. The trip through the jungle was difficult.

"It's not much farther now," Jessie kept telling little Lily, "and the boat will be waiting in Panama City."

But she was wrong. When they reached the city the harbor was empty. There were crowds of people in all the streets.

"Where are the boats?" Jessie asked one man.

"We don't know when a boat will come," he answered. "Gold has been found in California. People are rushing to the gold fields. They crowd on every ship bound for California. Once they get there, even the sailors desert. Few captains can get a crew for a return voyage. We're all stranded here. We've been here for weeks."

Jessie could only wait. During those weeks she received one letter, forwarded from Washington, from her husband. He had written from Kit Carson's ranch in New Mexico. He told her he was recovering from an illness. Now Jessie was even more anxious to continue her journey.

At last, after two months, a boat came. Jessie managed to get passage for herself and Lily. But when they landed in San Francisco, John was not there to meet them. Jessie was alarmed. Was her husband still sick?

A few days later John Frémont reached San Francisco. He was very thin and worn-looking and he limped. Jessie was sick, too, and had a bad cough. But they were alive and together. All three threw their arms around one another and laughed and cried and laughed again.

John talked about the ranch, which was named Mariposa. He had given a friend the money with which to buy it. Then the friend had bought the wrong piece of land. Instead of beautiful acres near the sea, they owned seventy square miles of rocky hills a hundred miles from the coast. "It's not even good grazing land," John said sadly.

Jessie was not discouraged. "We probably wouldn't be good ranchers, anyway," she said. "But maybe there's gold in our hills!"

She was too sick now to travel to the ranch. Her cough grew worse. She needed to rest in a milder climate, so John decided to take her south to Monterey. The days were sunny there and the air was more healthful.

In Monterey the Frémonts had to live in two rented rooms. "We're lucky to be this comfortable," Jessie said.

Here Jessie made her first home. When she

looked at the big, bare rooms she sighed for the snowy linens, the lace curtains, the rugs and books and fine paintings she had left in Washington. But she didn't mope long. She asked John to go to San Francisco and buy what furnishings he could find.

He came back with bamboo chairs, a teakwood table, yards of red Chinese satin and a couple of big grizzly-bear rugs. Jessie made curtains out of the satin. She spread the rugs in front of the fireplaces. For table linen she took strips of unbleached muslin and cross-stitched them together with red embroidery silk. The family ate from porcelain dishes.

Jessie had hoped John would bring her trunks and boxes of books. But he brought bad news about these. All of Jessie's belongings had been lost in a fire on the San Francisco docks. She would have to make new clothes for herself and Lily. She had no patterns, and the cloth her husband brought was heavy and hard to sew. But she managed to make what they needed. Her only book now was a copy of *The Arabian Nights' Entertainment.* John had bought it in San Francisco for her birthday present.

In spite of their bad luck, Jessie found life in California interesting. It was almost like living in a foreign country. She loved Monterey, with its flowers and low adobe houses. She soon made friends with the Mexicans and Indians, as well as the Americans who lived there. There was an Army post in the town, and Captain William T. Sherman and other young officers were often guests in the Frémont rooms.

John spent much of his time looking for gold at Mariposa. One day he galloped into Monterey to tell Jessie he had discovered a rich vein on their property. As soon as their friends heard the good news, they hurried to congratulate the Frémonts on their good fortune.

"What wonderful luck!" said a young officer. "You'll be very wealthy, Mrs. Frémont."

"Yes, perhaps, but gold isn't much by itself. At the moment I'd rather have a good book."

"But now you can order thousands of books from the East. You can buy anything you want. Gold strikes will make California great."

"No," Jessie said thoughtfully, "gold won't make California great. Only free men can do that. California's gold isn't all in her streams and mountains. There is also gold in the sunlight, in the desert sands, in the fields of poppies.

"Why do you think people call my husband 'the Pathfinder'? Not because he found the path to riches. He endured many hardships to make the path easier for settlers coming west. They're coming to start a new life. All they ask is a chance to make a home with their own hands. When my husband first saw the entrance to San

Francisco Bay, he called it the Golden Gate. He saw it as the gateway to golden opportunity. The gold in the mountains will someday be gone. California's true wealth will be here forever."

SENATOR'S LADY FROM CALIFORNIA

The Frémonts had been in California only a few months when settlers began to talk about joining the Union. "Let's call a convention in Monterey and write a constitution. Then we'll ask to be admitted as one of the United States."

Delegates began to arrive in Monterey. Many stopped to see the Frémonts. They spoke of California's great future. They discussed the problems of a new state. Jessie often took part in these discussions. The men listened carefully to her, for they respected her opinions. She helped them decide just what should be in the constitution, to satisfy the needs of all the people.

After this convention, Californians had to choose a governor and men to serve as Senators and Representatives in Washington, D.C. When people talked about the candidates, John Charles Frémont was often mentioned for Senator.

"He raised the first American flag over California," said one man.

"Frémont's reports and maps encouraged many of us to come here," said another.

"He knows all our problems. He'd know how to take care of our interests in Washington."

But many other names were considered. California had many good leaders.

One dark, rainy night Jessie and Lily were sitting in front of the fire. Suddenly the door opened. Jessie jumped up and saw her husband, his clothes dripping from the heavy rain.

He laughed and called, "I wanted to be the first to greet Jessie Frémont, Senator's lady from the state of California." John had ridden, without stopping, seventy miles from San Jose, the new capital, to Monterey to tell her the news.

The Frémonts left California for Washington on New Year's Day. This trip was very different from Jessie's first voyage. Now she and her husband and Lily were all together.

In Washington they had a joyful reunion with the Benton family. The Frémonts saw all their old friends. They went to many parties.

On September 10, 1850, Jessie Benton Frémont sat in the Senate gallery. How many times she had watched her father from this same place! But today her eyes were on her husband. John Charles Frémont was being sworn in as Senator from the new state of California. Jessie remembered her father's words, "A Senator's job isn't easy." She thought, "Even so, I'm happy we could come to Capitol Hill. And I'm proud that we came as citizens of California."

DO YOU REMEMBER?

1. When and where was Jessie Benton born?
2. Why was she called Jessie Anne?
3. How did Jessie manage to make herself heard on the day she was born?
4. Why did Jessie's family move to Washington, D.C., every winter?
5. What made Jessie decide to live alone when she was about seven years old?
6. On what kind of boat did Jessie and her family travel when they visited St. Louis?
7. Where did Jessie decide that she wanted to live when she grew up?
8. How did Jessie spend her time on her first visit to Capitol Hill with her father?
9. Why was Jessie so interested in Sam Houston the first time she met him?
10. Why couldn't Jessie wear her new dress the day her family visited President Jackson?
11. What interests did Jessie have that made her different from most girls of her time?
12. Why didn't Jessie like Daniel Webster?

13. What happened to make Jessie remember that she should not turn her back on the Mississippi?

14. How could Jessie tell when she was coming close to Grandma Benton's house?

15. Why did Jessie's parents decide to send her away to a boarding school?

16. Why was 1841 one of the most important years in Jessie's life?

17. What did Jessie do to help her husband in his work as an explorer?

18. How did Jessie feel about becoming a citizen of California?

IMPORTANT THINGS TO LOOK UP

1. How long was Jessie's father a United States Senator, and why was he given the nickname of "Old Bullion"?

2. What men served as Presidents of our country during Jessie's lifetime?

3. What was the Gold Rush in California, and how did it change Jessie's life?

4. What kind of work did Jessie do when her husband lost his fortune in the 1870's?

INTERESTING THINGS TO DO

1. Gather all the information you can about the kinds of clothes people wore when Jessie was a girl. Make some drawings of the wardrobe you think Jessie may have had.

2. Make a study of steamboats that were used in the 1830's. Draw an accurate picture of one of these steamboats and write a story about a boy or girl traveling down the Mississippi on this boat.

3. Learn all you can about the duties of a United States Senator. List the achievements of Senator Benton, and tell whether you think he would have been a good Senator today or not.

4. Find out all you can about the different expeditions John Charles Frémont made into the West. Trace the route of each expedition on a map of the United States.

OTHER BOOKS TO READ

Andrew Jackson, Clara Ingram Judson. Follett.

California Gold Rush, May McNeer. Follett.

Children of the Covered Wagon, Mary Jane Carr. Crowell.

John Charles Frémont, Trailmaker of the Old West, Olive Burt. Messner.

Kit Carson: Boy Trapper, Augusta Stevenson. Trade and School Editions, Bobbs-Merrill.

They Explored, Rhoda Huff and Helmut deTerra. Henry Z. Walck.

They Lived in the White House, Francis Cavanah. Macrae Smith.

U.S. Means Us, Nina Turner. Houghton.

Winning of the West, The, Harold McCracken. Garden City.

WHEN JESSIE FREMONT LIVED

1824   JESSIE ANNE BENTON WAS BORN, MAY 31.

There were 24 states in the Union.

The population of the country was about 10,000,000.

James Monroe was President.

1825–   JESSIE GREW UP IN WASHINGTON, D.C., VIR-
1841   GINIA, AND MISSOURI.

The Erie Canal was completed, 1825.

Andrew Jackson was President, 1829–1837.

Samuel Morse invented the telegraph, 1835.

American settlers reached Oregon, 1836.

Martin Van Buren was President, 1837–1841.

1841–
1850
JESSIE MARRIED JOHN CHARLES FREMONT, AND LATER MOVED TO CALIFORNIA.

The United States acquired the Oregon Territory south of the forty-ninth parallel, 1846.

The Mexican War was fought, 1846–1848.

Gold was discovered in California, 1848.

California became a state, 1850.

1851–
1870
JESSIE HELPED HER HUSBAND IN HIS WORK.

Harriet Beecher Stowe's *Uncle Tom's Cabin* was published, 1852.

Abraham Lincoln was President, 1861–1865.

The War between the States was fought, 1861–1865.

President Lincoln issued the Emancipation Proclamation, 1863.

The Thirteenth Amendment to the Constitution, forbidding slavery, was ratified, 1865.

The first transcontinental railroad was completed, 1869.

1870–   JESSIE ACHIEVED FAME AND HONOR AS A
1890   WRITER.

Alexander Bell invented the telephone, 1876.

Bicycles were first made in this country, 1878.

Thomas Edison invented the phonograph, 1878, and the electric light bulb, 1879.

Clara Barton founded the American Red Cross, 1881.

1902   JESSIE BENTON FREMONT DIED, DECEMBER 27.

There were 45 states in the Union.

The population of the country was about 76,000,000.

Theodore Roosevelt was President.

HELP WITH WORDS

adobe (*a* dō′bĭ) : sun-dried brick. Many people in southwestern United States and in Mexico live in adobe houses.

brocaded (brò kād′ĕd) : having raised designs woven on it, usually on silk cloth

cambric (kām′brĭk) : thin cotton or linen cloth

candidate (kăn′dĭ dāt) : one who offers himself, or is put forward by others, for an office or honor

198

cathedral (kȧ thē′drăl) : official church of a bishop; large or important church

channel (chăn′ĕl) : long narrow body of water joining two larger bodies of water

cholera (kŏl′ēr ȧ) : dangerous disease which spreads quickly and usually causes death. There is now a vaccine to control cholera.

Congress (kŏng′grĕs) : the national lawmaking body of the United States, composed of the Senate and the House of Representatives

constitution (kŏn′stĭ tū′shŭn) : principles and laws which are used to govern a state or society. The United States has a written constitution, as does every state in the Union.

convention (kŏn vĕn′shŭn) : meeting arranged for some special purpose, such as choosing candidates for office, or writing a constitution

coronet (kŏr ȯ nĕt′) : circle of gold, jewels, or flowers worn on the head as ornament

delirious (dė lĭr′ĭ ŭs) : out of one's senses, raving, wildly excited

diplomat (dĭp′lō măt) : person who works to bring about pleasant relations between nations

expedition (ĕks′pė dĭsh′ŭn) : trip or journey for some special purpose, usually for exploring

floating dock: dock which floats on the water. It can be partly sunk to let a ship sail into it, and afterward floated to raise the ship high and dry.

gallery (găl′ẽr ĭ) : a balcony looking down into a long hall, or room

isthmus (ĭs′mŭs) : narrow strip of land with water on both sides, which connects two larger bodies of land

levee (lĕv′ė̇) : bank or wall built to keep a river from overflowing

missionary (mĭsh′ŭn ẽr ĭ) : one who is sent to tell other people about a religion and try to make them believe in it

orator (ŏr′a̍ tẽr) : public speaker

Oregon Trail (ŏr′ė̇ gŭn) : route followed by people moving into western United States, mainly between 1804 and 1846. It started at Independence, Missouri and was about 2,000 miles long

overseer (ō′vẽr sē′ẽr) : one who is in charge of workers and inspects the work done

reception (rė̇ sĕp′shŭn) : party at which a special person is introduced; entertainment after a wedding so that guests may congratulate the newly-married couple

seminary (sĕm′ĭ nẽr ĭ) : private high school